RITA HAYWORTH

A MEMOIR

by James Hill

SIMON AND SCHUSTER

NEW YORK

Copyright © 1983 by James Hill
All rights reserved
including the right of reproduction
in whole or in part in any form
Published by Simon and Schuster
A Division of Gulf & Western Corporation
Simon & Schuster Building
Rockefeller Center
1230 Avenue of the Americas
New York, New York 10020

SIMON AND SCHUSTER and colophon are
registered trademarks of Simon & Schuster
Designed by Eve Kirch
Manufactured in the United States of America

10 9 8 7 6 5 4 3 2 1

Library of Congress Cataloging in Publication Data

Hill, James, date.
   Rita Hayworth, a memoir.
   1. Hayworth, Rita 2. Moving-picture
actors and actresses—United States—Biography.
I. Title.
PN2287.H38H54 1983   791.43'028'0924 [B]   82-19522
ISBN 0-671-43273-7

PART ONE

ON that particular morning, I found my friend Harry Clork leaving his house with his daughter. They lived in Brentwood, which is a nifty residential section of West Los Angeles. So while I was trying to get a word in about the catastrophe that had befallen me in New York over the weekend, Harry was having all kinds of trouble with this six-year-old child of his.

I would have told the child to get lost, or do something constructive like get a paper route, if it had been me, but old Harry was playing the heavy Freudian father, a role he loved. The cause of all the trouble between them was her swiping a Christmas present from a girlfriend's house. This had prompted Harry to write a touching speech of apology, which she was now rehearsing on the way to returning the stolen gift.

I never let myself come right to the heart of a matter, because if there is anything I can't stand it's people who feel sorry for themselves, which was why I had determined on an oblique approach.

"I guess what's worrying me most is Peggy," I would say. "After practically living with her for a year, and having her pin her hopes on marriage, then for this to happen over the weekend . . ." I would sort of let my voice trail off, knowing Harry would ask, "What happened?" Then I'd tell him about the catastrophe, and instead of feeling sorry for ourselves, we'd wind up feeling sorry for poor Peggy.

Only before I had a chance to launch into it, we had moved up the walk to this two-story New England colonial that was hidden from the road by the trees. I could see it was no time to interrupt Harry, who was being very stern with his kid. He was even using a side of

Freud I had never seen him fall back on before. He had doubled up his fist.

"I want to hear your speech," Harry said to his kid, "and I want it letter-perfect."

Well, the kid kind of hesitated, but seeing the way Harry was circling with his fist, she knocked off the speech, after which Harry nodded, pleased more with the ring of his words than her recitation. Then he pushed the bell.

The sound of the chimes inside brought an expectant smile to Harry's face, like a performer waiting for the curtains to part, but it also brought a vicious kick to his shin by his six-year-old daughter.

While Harry was doubling over in pain, she leaped off the porch. Immediately, Harry took off after her. I watched them disappear down the road, leaving me with the catastrophe of my New York trip still unexplained. And that was when the front door opened behind me.

I've had my share of surprises, but never anything like this, because if you had told me I could meet anybody I desired—and I don't mean just those living, but Babe Ruth or Bill Tilden or Bobby Jones, or even the Ball of Fire, who happened to be one sensational stripper —the lady presently gazing out at me would still have topped my list.

In spite of the old towel she had wrapped around her head, in spite of old baggy work jeans, even in spite of having no makeup on and a dripping scrub brush in her hand, she had these wide-set eyes like no one I had ever seen, which was probably why she was the most glamorous actress in the entire motion-picture business.

"I hope you know how to drive," she said in a low, soft voice, "because there's not only all the work to be done inside, but there're so many errands . . ."

It wasn't just that her eyes were so wide set, or the way they were flecked with changing colors, greens and golds, but there was a sadness there, like in the tale of the fairy princess, so that all you wanted to do was rescue her.

Anyway, I guess I just kept staring—I couldn't get over this really happening to me, and at such an early hour—when I became aware that she was still talking to me.

"You *are* from the agency, aren't you?"

Now there was no way I was going to endanger this newfound relationship with an honest answer to that question. If she had thought I was there to test for current in light sockets, I wouldn't have hesitated to risk a finger. Or even a firing squad, if she was worried about the vulnerability of a bulletproof vest.

I just knew I wanted to look and look into those eyes. So it never occurred to me to do anything but nod and smile. And the next thing, I was inside, on the floor with the scrub brush she'd had in her hand when she answered the door.

After she showed me how to use it with a professional circular motion, even getting down on her knees and all to demonstrate, I wanted to tell her what a miracle sort of thing it was to find her doing this, but I didn't dare for fear of frightening her, or what was worse, maybe waking up and discovering it *was* just a dream after all.

Once I got the circular motion down pat, she showed me a number of other chores, which included taking charge of the little stack of autographed pictures of her on the hall table by the front door. In this real shy way, she explained how people would sometimes ring the bell for one, and—with its being the day before Christmas—there would probably be more requests than usual.

There were a couple of other things she showed me that I didn't even remember, because of looking so deep into her eyes, and then I was back scrubbing again. I had worked my way from the living room into the dining room, where through the open kitchen door I could see her polishing silver.

She had these artistic hands with long, slender fingers. I found myself wishing I was a piece of that silver, and how nice it would be to have her polish me. That got me to thinking about how hard it would be later to make anybody believe that this really was Miss Hayworth, since here we were—scrubbing and polishing like any ordinary couple, who might even have been married.

If I forgot to mention her name before, it's because once I told you about her eyes, I knew you'd already have guessed. Anyway, I speeded up my circular motion, so in no time flat I had worked my way into the kitchen and had scrubbed all around her until she stood like she was on this last tiny bit of dry land.

I couldn't help noticing that she had that sad, faraway look in her eyes again. In spite of my nearness, she was totally unaware of me, which made me kind of smile, because of what I had in mind.

"I guess I'll just have to carry you to dry land," I was going to say, "since you'd better not risk a crossing on these slippery shores." Once I had her in my arms, I planned to add, "I got so carried away with my work, I forgot about your being there."

I suppose what made me hesitate was wanting to be classier, since I must admit this approach could sound a little corny. Anyway, I blew it, because right then this barracuda came swimming in through the front of the house, and I mean with fangs exposed.

As the day wore on, I discovered Miss Hayworth was surrounded by nothing but these types, but the first one to arrive was her black housekeeper, who lived there with her husband. Only on this particular morning, her husband had turned up missing from their bed, and she had just come back from making out a report at the police station.

She no sooner spotted me than she started haranguing the Good People Employment Agency for having sent out a man when she had specifically requested a woman, which right away explained how she felt about men, and also was a clear clue to why her husband walked in his sleep.

I never paused in my scrubbing, so I can't tell you how relieved I was when she finally took her eyes off me and joined Miss Hayworth in polishing the silver.

All the while she continued lamenting the treachery of men, and she didn't stop with her husband, but included this man who had been going with Miss Hayworth. He was some kind of a prince I'd been reading about in the papers, whose father got his weight in diamonds every year from his subjects.

Anyway, he was supposed to have shown up for the Christmas holidays, but hadn't, and the barracuda seemed to take a malicious delight in informing Miss Hayworth that he had read in a supermarket scandal sheet that the Prince was spending Christmas skiing in the Alps.

I guess what made me want to do something special for her was the way she never took exception to what the old barracuda was saying, or ordered her out of the house, which was what I would have done if I'd been paying her salary.

I had scrubbed my way into the den during this conversation, which gave me the opportunity of slipping to the hall telephone. Now that I had the name of the agency, I gave them a ring and told them I was calling for Miss Hayworth. I can't tell you the effect that name had; the head of the agency came on immediately, assuring me that the help Miss Hayworth requested was on the way.

Gawd!

I still had the scrub brush in my hand when I answered the doorbell that first time, wondering how I'd handle it if the caller was from the agency, although I didn't forget to pick up an autographed picture from the table just in case.

There stood Harry's daughter, who was now being subjected to yet another aspect of behavior modification—a tight grip by Harry on the braid she wore down her back. Right away she went into her speech, which made Harry give her pigtail such a yank even Freud would have been proud. "Not to him, you jerk!" he shouted over her yelp. "He's not your friend's mother, is he?"

"Uncle Jim!" she cried in startled recognition.

"What are you doing answering the door, for crissake?" Harry said. "You know the mother, or something?"

The last thing I wanted was for Harry to discover who *really* lived here, or I figured I might never get rid of him. "It was a surprise to me, but I know the housekeeper," I said, trying not to shudder at the thought of the barracuda.

Harry noticed the brush in my hand. "She's got you scrubbing, has she?"

I gave him my best lascivious leer. "That and other things."

Any intimation of sexual involvement brought an immediate smile to Harry's face. He was a firm believer that if you were sexually engaged, you and your work had to prosper.

"Scrubbing away your cares with the housekeeper, are you?" Harry grinned.

"When the cat's away—" I shrugged, and was about to tell him the lady of the house wouldn't be back until New Year's when his eyes almost popped right out of his skull, which told me without looking who had materialized behind me.

At the sight of her, Harry's daughter launched into her speech about the Christmas spirit, and how badly she felt about stealing the present, but even before she was halfway through, Miss Hayworth interrupted with that soft, soft voice of hers—the voice that made everything become so still.

"I understand," Miss Hayworth said. "It's a music box I got for my daughter. She's spending Christmas in Rome with her father. She'll be getting so many presents"—she broke off—"I'd like you to have it."

I watched her eyes mist. Whatever she was seeing, it wasn't the look of delight she had brought to the face of Harry Clork's daughter.

At the time, I didn't begin to read the significance of that look, or of the tragedy behind it. All I was thinking was how the moment I saw her I had known I wanted to do something special for her, and now I knew what it was. I wanted to see her smile.

In all the years of working with him, this was the first time I found old Harry without words. He was that overcome by her unexpected appearance. So before he got to speculating any further on my presence there, I was quick to follow her inside, and even quicker to close the door behind us.

One of the things I couldn't help noticing in that antiseptic house was the total lack of any holiday decorations: no tree or wreath—not even a little sprig of holly.

They were in the kitchen finishing up the silver, while I was in the next room, where the barracuda had me waxing the floors I'd scrubbed. I hadn't been paying close attention to their conversation, since I had been racking my brain to find the key to a smile.

"I know it sounds strange, but whenever I think of Christmas, I think of caviar and iced vodka," Miss Hayworth was saying. "I was dancing in Caliente on Christmas Eve. A party of four sent us a hundred-dollar tip, but it wasn't that. It was the *elegance* of the women in their furs and the men in their white ties and tails—and the flow of iced vodka and caviar, and the wonderful toasts. In spite of the crowd, they seemed to be in a world apart, and they made happiness something full of style."

That was the most I had heard Miss Hayworth say to date, so I managed to wax my way right up to the kitchen door.

"I was thirteen," Miss Hayworth went on, "and the evening was still ahead of me." Then her voice got even lower, so I had to strain to hear her, and a kind of breathless excitement crept into it. "The waiters never bothered clearing the tables after the crowd had gone, so when the lights were out I slipped to that special table, and I had my first taste of caviar, and I toasted myself with my first iced vodka."

Even though I couldn't see her, I knew that mist would be coming into her eyes because of the faraway note in her voice, like when she gave the present to Harry's kid.

I was hoping she'd reveal what her toast to herself had been, but she didn't. So when the barracuda started cranking up about a child of thirteen drinking vodka when she should have been in church, my mind went back to Miss Hayworth's mention of Caliente and her dancing there. You see, it was in Caliente that I had first run into her, even though she hadn't remembered me when she came to the door.

We had been taking one of those weekend trips to historic places that my father thought were educational and that my mother loved because they meant getting out of the house and away from the cooking. Since we had just recently moved to Los Angeles from Seattle, the very thought of crossing the border into Mexico was of going into another world.

I had heard you could buy women down there, which, since I had just turned fifteen, was one of the things most on my mind in those days. I had also heard the place was evil, which happened to be about the only other thing that preoccupied me, besides tennis and basketball, that is.

So I had made my father believe it was his idea to visit this famous mission between Tijuana and Agua Caliente, because if he knew how much I really cared about history, we'd never have gotten out of our backyard.

The mission turned out to be a couple of crumbling walls with this sleepy guide, who even I couldn't understand, although I was in my second year of high-school Spanish. Anyway, with the historical part of the trip and lunch behind us, we wound up at a gambling casino. It featured a couple known as the Dancing Cansinos, which happened to be Miss Hayworth's family name before she became famous.

Since my mother hardly drank at all, I was busy putting away this fancy rum concoction of hers, while she watched the dancers. "That girl can't be any older than Jimmy," my mother said.

It was the first real whiff of evil I'd gotten. If my mother was right, the girl had to be no more than fifteen—or maybe fourteen, or even thirteen—which meant the man dancing with her, who was supposed to be her husband but looked easily three times as old, had to be displaying her on the floor for a price.

Earlier, when we had been playing the slot machines, I had eased away from my family and over to this kid who roamed the floor making change, and asked if there were any women available.

"There's none of 'em working here that *don't* have a price," he told me confidentially.

I had twenty-five dollars on me, which I had saved up from my paper route for this very purpose, and although I hated the thought of paying a middleman, I decided this was the time to close a deal. The only concern I had was my folks. I was thinking seriously of simply disappearing, and then later saying how easy it was to lose each other in a foreign land, when my brother, who was three years younger than I was, reminded my parents they had promised to take him to the bullfights.

Now the only thing my brother could do well was throw a baseball farther than just about anyone else, which hardly seemed a reason to turn the rest of the afternoon over to him, but that's just what my father did.

Anyway, no sooner did they start placing their darts into the dilapidated old bull than my brother got sick at the sight of all the blood, so my mother had to take him out. Then my father and I got feeling queasy, too. Only instead of finding my mother and brother in the car when we came out, we found them in a whorehouse.

Naturally, my mother had no idea where she was, because she right away started telling us how these wonderful girls had seen Dave being sick by the car, and had brought them inside. To hear my mother, it was like discovering a world of Florence Nightingales, but I could tell my father had accurately assessed the situation.

You can see how I had finally hit the jackpot, but also why I had to move fast. There was one older lady, who I figured must be the madam, and although I was plenty nervous, I managed to draw her off to one side. I flashed the old twenty-five-dollar bankroll and gave her a knowing wink.

Well, you'll never believe this, but the madam got all uptight. She wanted to know what kind of a son I was to have such a wonderful mother and to be thinking such rotten thoughts. The way she started raising her voice I was afraid she was going to draw my folks' attention, even though they were busy getting my brother back on his feet, so I quickly beat it outside.

Now I had my second stroke of luck, because who should be turning the corner, and alone, but the very same girl we saw dancing earlier. I figured without the old guy around I was a cinch to make a better deal, so I eased a ten off my roll. But I never got around to flashing it, because of the frightened look in her eyes, like you see when a fawn is running from a fire.

In the next moment I was plenty glad I hadn't, because the old guy came striding around the corner, and he was bigger than I had remembered. She hadn't gone more than a step or two past me, when he caught up to her and grabbed her by the wrist.

"Did that boy speak to you?" he asked sternly.

"No, father," she said.

Then his tone got even colder and angrier as they moved off. "I've told you *never* to call me father down here," he said. "I have also told you never to leave the club without me. I don't want to have to discipline you, so make sure it doesn't happen again."

You can see why I could hardly expect her to have remembered me from that first time I saw her, and it wasn't until years later, when I had become a writer, and made a sort of reputation as a drugstore analyst, that I came to realize one thing about that first encounter.

It's amazing how many successful people grow up without ever having had a youth. If you take those childhood years and have to spend them doing five shows a day in a shabby place like Caliente with a man you have to pretend is your husband but is really your father, it becomes easy to understand why a person might well have a sad, faraway look in her eyes.

So even though I was only waxing her floors—no more than a menial in her eyes—I suddenly saw what I could do for her. I could give her the youth she'd never had. Since most people (including Peggy, the southern girl I was supposed to marry) thought I had never outgrown my own, you can see that I was especially well equipped to lead someone down that path.

Naturally, I wasn't so dumb as to think I could just say, "Miss Hayworth, I'm prepared to give you the youth you never had—just as soon as I finish waxing this floor." Instead, I remembered that I had forty dollars in my pocket: two twenties to be exact. While that sum would hardly buy her emeralds, it *would* buy some caviar and iced vodka, like she remembered from that long-ago Christmas in Caliente.

I have to admit I'm a much better conversationalist with a little vodka in me, even when it's not iced, although I'm not too big on caviar. But you can see how my fantasy was running—my toasting her in Stolichnaya, her wanting to know after that first toast who I *really* was, which would lead into my telling her, and then, of course, our turning back the clock. So while I may have been down on my knees, I was actually riding a cloud.

In telling you about what happened next, I remind you about the barracuda's being merely the forerunner of the deadly types infesting those waters. I'm referring to the passel of lawyers who arrived at that point to discuss raising the alimony from the husband she was divorced from.

I had been a kind of admirer of Orson Welles, until he married her. Then he seemed to spend most of his time sawing her in half in his magic act—when, that is, he wasn't consuming whole lambs or barbecued pigs, or other gourmand's delights that were making him bigger and bigger. At any rate, Orson Welles did, after all, have something of a reputation as an actor and director, so I couldn't blame her for marrying him. Especially if she made the mistake of thinking she was getting some kind of a father figure.

Unfortunately, Miss Hayworth wasn't showing too much interest in her alimony. That's when I realized the lawyers were using it as an excuse to get her to sign papers giving them power of attorney, which meant they could write checks on her bank accounts without consulting her.

"Miss Hayworth?" I cried without thinking, as I moved into the den, which caused her to pause with the pen in her hand. It also caused the passel of piranhas to glare, since I still had the waxing equipment with me.

"Yes . . . ?" Miss Hayworth said, looking up at me with those extraordinary eyes.

I knew in the silence that followed I would seal my own doom if I spoke my piece. Imagine just trying to explain what made me—the freelance floor-waxer—such an authority on fraud.

"Miss Hayworth," I finally said, "I'm running short of autographed photos."

"Gee-suss!" a voice said in total exasperation.

Even I had to admit it was a pretty dumb excuse to barge in like I had, but Miss Hayworth never gave the voice so much as a glance.

"I'll tell you what we'll do. From now on we'll only give them to the children who have been eating properly. That's what I usually do, anyway." She turned to the piranhas. "There's nothing more important than good nutrition, don't you think?"

It killed me the way she always had to get your approval, which I could understand in my case, but all these others, Gawd! "I'm a big believer in good nutrition myself," I said.

"Gee-suss!" that same voice said again, and most of the others joined in.

"Well," Miss Hayworth said, "you just see that *they* do, too."

I can't tell you what it did to me, looking into those gentle eyes of hers, then having to watch her pick up that pen again, while I had no choice but to go helplessly back to my waxing. I was afraid she'd give the house away before I even had a chance to come up with the caviar and vodka, let alone get around to restoring her youth.

Of course, the worst was yet to come, because the next time the chimes rang, and I picked up an autographed picture, who should be standing there but a girl from the Good People Employment Agency. Since she practically had a foot inside the door, I did the only thing

I could think of, which was to bring out the two twenties from my pocket. "I'm terribly sorry," I said, "but Miss Hayworth has already found someone."

"She should have called the agency and told them."

"Miss Hayworth is a generous person," I said. "I know she wouldn't have wanted you to come out here for nothing." I was wondering if I could get away with just giving her five, although it meant asking her to break a twenty, but it would still have left me thirty-five for the caviar and vodka.

"It's usual to give a full day's pay," the girl said, "if you don't call back within the hour and cancel."

I swallowed hard. "A day's pay . . . ?"

"At two-fifty an hour, it comes to twenty dollars," she said. "That's the going rate for an ordinary domestic."

"I see."

"No, I don't think you do, not in my case," she said. "I am *not* an ordinary domestic. I only took this assignment because I wanted to meet Miss Hayworth."

"I'm afraid that's impossible," I said. "So you'll have to be satisfied with the twenty."

She smiled—really a very sexy smile. "We'll see," she said, taking the twenty. "Do you live with her?"

"Why . . . ?"

"If you live with her that's one thing, but if you work for her that's another," she said. "You look like you live with her. You're kind of cute."

I was beginning to lose my cool. "Yes, I do."

"Live with her . . . ?"

"Yes."

"Then you sleep with her?"

All I needed was for Miss Hayworth to walk in on that one, but I was afraid if I closed the door she might do something rash. "Look now—" I began in my sternest voice, when she interrupted.

"How important is that other twenty to you?"

"Very!" I snapped.

"Well, if you really want to get rid of me, you'll have to give it to me, but I'll tell you how you can get it back."

"How?"

"You'll have to sleep with me."

I couldn't believe it! "You'd *pay* me to sleep with you?"

A kind of wistfulness came into her voice. "I guess that's as close as I'll ever get to her."

After the barracuda, the piranhas, and now this girl, who had to be some kind of a nut, I was left almost speechless. "You mean you want to sleep with the person who's sleeping with her?" I said. "You'd settle for that?"

"I've seen every one of her pictures a million times," she said, not in the least embarrassed. "I guess I'm in love with her."

I gave her the other twenty, but when she asked for something to write her phone number on, I told her to forget it. As badly as I wanted that twenty back—because there went the vodka and caviar —I figured there was no way I could collect it on those terms.

Inside the house again, I found Miss Hayworth with her old friend Earl Felton, who had come in through the rear. Felton was one of the better-known screenwriters; he'd had polio as a kid and had to walk with canes. He was telling her how one of his braces wasn't working properly, which was playing havoc with his Christmas shopping. I know I should have been more sympathetic, but I was wishing she'd throw him out—like I had everyone else who'd been around her— when she suggested that I drive his car, and carry his packages for him. If it hadn't been for that look in her eyes, I would have walked out right then, since I was still just a menial to her, and what was worse, a menial without a plan.

She must have noticed something, because she quickly said that once I got back, she would write me out a check. How much more depressed could I get; no sooner did she become aware of me than she was getting rid of me.

That was when the chimes sounded again and everything began to turn around for me, and from a most unlikely source.

I picked up an autographed picture and who did I find standing outside, but Harry Cohn. I can't believe there's anyone who hasn't heard of Harry Cohn, because he was head of Columbia Pictures, the studio that had Miss Hayworth under contract. He also had a terrible reputation for being a tyrant, but since I've never been one to prejudge another, I was prepared to like him—until he opened his mouth.

"Tell Hayworth I'm here!"

The way he said it was bad enough, but when I hesitated, he started to shove past me, which really made me burn. I've always had a thing about good manners, so I pretended not to know who he was.

"I'm sorry, sir," I said, politeness itself, "but if you would like an autographed picture of Miss Hayworth, you'll have to deal with me."

He was short and heavyset with a pretty good gut, so it was easy enough for me to block his path. He got red in the face, and I thought maybe he was going to have a stroke.

"What the hell do you think you're doing, you asshole!" Mr. Cohn roared, still trying to push past me.

"I'm afraid, sir, I didn't make myself clear," I said, not giving an inch. "You may be off one of those expensive tour buses, but you'll still have to abide by the rules." I didn't think he could get any more apoplectic, but he did.

"You goddamn punk, do you know who the hell I *am?*"

"I only know you haven't been eating properly"—and I paused to take a good look at his gut—"and since it is Miss Hayworth's expressed wish that I only give autographed pictures—"

"You stupid sonofabitch!" he swore at me, before turning to shout in the direction of his limousine, "Louie!"

I didn't know who Louie was, but I had an idea even before he came busting through the shrubbery. He had to be the biggest, toughest, meanest-looking chauffeur I had ever seen, and I couldn't have been happier at the sight.

"Cream this goddamn crumb, Louie!" Mr. Cohn screamed.

I didn't even bother putting up my fists as this giant strode toward me, because I really wanted him to bust me one. When my nose was broken and my whole face splattered with blood, I could imagine the look it would bring to Miss Hayworth's eyes; and then, naturally, we'd have to go off to the bathroom together, where she'd use those nifty fingers of hers to take a damp cloth to what was left of my features.

"Louie! Please!"

The giant chauffeur was just pulling back his fist, when he froze at the sound of her voice. Mr. Cohn glared at her. "Where did you find this stupid sonofabitch!"

There wasn't too much doubt about who Mr. Cohn was referring to, but I pretended to look around, which made his face go all red again, since I believe he was even unhappier than I was that Louie hadn't clobbered me.

"I'm talking about you, you crumb!" He even jabbed a finger at me, as if there might still be some doubt. Then he whirled back on Miss Hayworth. "I asked you a question, goddammit!"

Those eyes of hers were like they were the first time I told you about, when she reminded me of a fawn running from a fire. "He happens to be a valued employee." I could see how much courage it took for her to stand up to this man.

"You fucking him?"

Her voice was so low it was almost a whisper, but she still kept her poise. "Yes."

"Liar!" he snorted. "I'm going to give you one last chance, Hayworth. You can join me and the family at the Springs for the holidays. You'll have your own bedroom, where you can sleep alone for a change." The way he laughed made it obvious he planned on visiting that bedroom. "And don't give me that bullshit about being busy, because that prince of yours is fucking his brains out with some model in the Alps."

She paled at this, because he had really hit her where it hurt, but she didn't fold. "He's skiing."

"If you can fuck on skis, then he's skiing. So get your goddamn diaphragm and get your ass in my car."

I thought for sure she was going to break then, because of the way her lower lip trembled. "I'm busy, Mr. Cohn."

"How many times have I told you not to call me Mr. Cohn!" he bellowed. "I've tried to be nice to you. I've tried to treat you like a lady, but you've done nothing but piss on my offers of friendship. And don't think it's not going to affect the parts offered you!" He glared at each one of us in turn, his chauffeur, then Miss Hayworth, then me. "What's that silly sonofabitch grinning about? *Ask* him!"

"What are you grinning about?" Miss Hayworth said.

"I was wondering if you wanted me to give him an autographed picture?" I said.

Her lip stopped trembling then, and her voice became the loudest I had ever heard it, which still wasn't much above a whisper. "Not with his stomach."

If ever I just wanted to hug someone, I mean truly hug them, it was her right then. But she quickly turned back into the living room, and I could tell she was going to crack, because I could hear her footsteps rushing up the stairs.

Earl Felton was feeling no pain when we arrived at Bleary's Liquor Emporium, the last stop on our shopping tour. He had been nipping steadily ever since it had started to rain. The place was empty and about to close, not because of the hour, but because of its being Christmas Eve. All I could think of was Miss Hayworth as she fled the crassness of Harry Cohn.

Felton had been ranging down the shelves of merchandise on his canes. Out of the corner of my eye, I watched him filch a quart and slip it into one of the big pockets of his raincoat. Suddenly, inspiration hit me, and I turned to the owner.

"I'd keep an eye on that crippled fellow," I told the owner, who was busy at the cash register totaling his receipts. "I believe he's shoplifting."

"Why, I'll be goddamned, there goes a can of my best pâté . . . and a fifth of Black Label . . . I'll call the police!"

"I wouldn't do that if I were you. That happens to be Earl Felton, who's obviously been drinking."

"Pelton . . . ?"

I shook my head. "Felton. The distinguished screenwriter and Oscar winner," I said, although I may have been exaggerating about the Oscar. "You could ruin your place with the picture clientele, what with his being so famous, and crippled, and all."

The owner paused in his dialing, and looked at me accusingly. "You came in with him. Can't *you* do something?"

"I'm only driving him," I said. "You see, I work for Miss Hayworth."

Like everyone else, he was impressed by that name, but only briefly, because of Felton's next maneuver. "Good Christ, he's into the tinned butter cookies from Denmark! . . . And there goes a bottle of Remy Martin!" His voice became a wail. "What am I going to *do?*"

I moved closer and dropped my voice even lower, almost like putting a comforting arm around him. "Have your two assistants keep an eye on him from behind the freezer windows and make a list of everything he steals, while you do the same from the opposite side of the floor as if you're taking inventory. Then deliver an itemized bill by hand, which I guarantee he will pay pronto, once he's sobered up and realizes the scandal you've saved him."

"A famous Oscar-winning movie writer, and crippled! I'd never have believed it," he mused. "I can't tell you how grateful I am."

"You've saved yourself an embarrassing situation," I said. "That's all I'm worried about."

"No, before leaving, I want you to select a gift on me—anything in the store that takes your fancy, and I'll send it over. I'm a great admirer of Miss Hayworth's."

Of course once he had deployed his two assistants and taken up his fake inventory station, it left his most exclusive stock exposed, imported Beluga caviar. It was stacked almost to the ceiling on a display table, and what made it so nifty, at least to me, was that the other item featured just happened to be that formidably expensive 110-proof Russian vodka. Talk about your luck turning!

When I finally staggered out of Bleary's Liquor Emporium, I thought I might develop a hernia from the weight of all the pound tins of caviar in the pockets of my raincoat and the several quarts of Stolichnaya tucked inside my belt.

Anyway, the owner was wearing a self-satisfied smile, which I made even broader by indicating the gift he'd asked me to select, and so, with lots of Merry Christmases all around, we departed.

On the drive back, Felton never referred to his shoplifting spree, but when he asked for my address, I could tell that he planned on dropping off for me one of the cheaper items as a Christmas present.

If I do say so myself, I always try to be fair. So knowing the whopping bill he was going to get, I told him how I hate the holidays, because someone was always giving you a gift, which made you feel you had to give them one in return. He was so relieved that when I got out from behind the wheel back at Miss Hayworth's, he slid right under it, and without so much as a thank you, or even a Merry Christmas, he drove off.

Once I got my raincoat hung up in the hall closet, I stashed the Russian vodka along with the tins of the Beluga caviar in the kitchen. I had to be wearing a smile from ear to ear, when I became aware of Miss Hayworth. I don't know how long she'd been standing there, but it was like she had become really aware of me for the first time.

"You let me believe you were from the agency," she said. And she said it like I'd broken the scout's oath, or worse.

"Yes, I did. I was so surprised when you answered the door, I didn't know what to do," I said. "You see, I owe my whole career to you, so when I realized you needed someone to scrub the floors, I felt in a small way I could begin to repay that debt."

I knew I had to say something to catch her, as corny as it may have sounded.

"I don't understand." She looked puzzled. "I mean about your career and me."

That was all the opening I needed. I explained how it had been my senior year in college and I was home for Easter vacation. There was an elegant private residential section in Los Angeles called Fremont Place. I was cutting through it, when I saw an old girlfriend getting out of a Rolls. I watched her join a film company that was shooting in front of a fabulous mansion. She was wearing a magnificent gown and furs. I watched them setting lights up all around her, and I overheard somebody explain that she was just the stand-in for the star.

"Dorothy Dumont," Miss Hayworth said. "I knew it had to be her when you mentioned the Rolls."

"Then there's not much more I can tell you about that set that you don't already know," I said. "Because the next moment, the star of the picture came onto the scene—and that was you."

"Oh, dear," she sort of sighed. "It was such a dreadful picture."

"Not to me," I said. "All of a sudden that afternoon turned into something magical. I had never been on a set before, and it was like some kind of fantasy watching you and all the other actors. But especially you, because you became another person entirely."

She frowned at that, which I somehow knew she would, but the ice was broken at last, and I found myself telling her about our trip to Caliente, and of the shy, frightened girl I had seen dancing down there. I purposely never mentioned her father, but I almost told her about wanting to make a deal for her because I figured it might make her laugh. Instead, I wound up telling her how once those cameras had started rolling, it was like electricity the way her personality lit everything up. The last thing she did that day was dance the bolero wearing a black broad-brimmed hat and with castanets. For me it was like being transported to another world. I didn't even remember saying goodbye to Dorothy Dumont. All I knew was I *had* to be a part of that world. So when I got back to college I took a course in playwriting, the first course I ever took seriously. I'd discovered there was no better way to break into the movie business than as a writer. And while it didn't happen overnight, it happened—if you can call a junior writer a writer, I added with a smile.

One of the true arts is a talent for listening. Of course, the threat of the guillotine couldn't have stopped me. And then looking into those eyes of hers didn't slow me down any, either. Although I have to admit, I took her by surprise when I finally paused. I mean it was a long moment before she fully realized that and began to collect herself. Which is another sign of a great listener. Knowing when to collect yourself.

"Mr. Clork told me you had the talent to be a fine writer," she said.

"Harry was here?" I said, amazed, since I had been that sure it was the fan with the sex fantasies who had somehow tipped her off about me. "Harry Clork . . . ?"

"Yes, he was worried about you," Miss Hayworth said. "He told me you had suffered a crisis over the weekend that you hadn't even told him about."

Good old Harry, I thought to myself, *he couldn't stand not getting a rundown*, but I could see from her concern that he had come through for me in his way.

"It was only a job I was fired from," I said, trying to make it sound offhand, even though it had been a real catastrophe.

"You're such a good worker," she said. "It's hard to believe you were fired."

To show you what a little flattery can do from a person with eyes like hers and a gift for listening, I immediately launched into a full-dress account of my firing—I told her about the bastard who headed the television department of the ad agency where Harry and I were doing a weekly program. They had called me to New York and offered to make me the show's producer, when this s.o.b. who was my boss says right in front of the agency's owner, "Now that you've been promoted and are one of the big brass, what do you see as your next step up?"

I guess after all the abuse I'd taken from him, plus my hatred of television, I'd had it. So I told him, "I guess my next step would be your job."

Naturally, I never used the word bastard, but I didn't leave any doubt in her mind that that was what I meant. And I must have laid it on just right, because in that moment I could see the compassion in her eyes.

"Oh my!" she said first, then she gasped. She truly did. "My oh my oh my."

"When I returned to the coast, I found a wire waiting for me," I said, feeling it needed this last little fillip. "It said, 'You're fired.' "

"I'd be so proud, if just once I had that kind of nerve." She took a deep breath then, and sort of sighed. It's funny how something as small as a sigh can affect a person, because I suddenly felt so drained I had to sit down. "No wonder you're exhausted," she said, and sank down beside me like she was exhausted, too.

After just sort of looking at each other in this real relaxed way, she seemed the first to rally. "I can't get over this happening to you, and yet your first concern was helping me."

You may not believe this, but for the second time that day I said something that was the total truth—not that everything else hadn't had a *touch* of it, but this was without embroidery of any kind.

"You've made my Christmas," I said.

"No," she said. "I'd feel so much better if I could do something for you."

"I'll tell you what. I've got this last floor to finish up, then I'd love to have a drink before I leave." She frowned, and I felt for sure I had somehow overplayed my hand, so I quickly added, "If it's an inconvenience, forget it."

"It's not that," she said. "I'm afraid I gave Mr. Clork the last of the vodka."

You can imagine, what with the loot I had stashed in the closet, how that made me smile. "We'll make out," I said. "I'm sure we can find something."

The way her face lit up as she nodded, it was all I could do not to sound too happy. She told me she wanted to tidy herself up after all the work of getting the house in order, so she would be a few minutes, if I'd excuse her.

If I'd excuse her! Imagine!

Since she didn't walk, but floated, I watched her glide up the stairs, which meant I had nothing to look forward to on that Christmas Eve but iced vodka, caviar, and the undivided attention of the most glamorous star in the motion-picture business.

Even Maybelle, the barracuda, would have marveled at how fast that wax got on the floor. Then I dashed into the john that was off the entry hall. I set another record in the way I washed up, splashed some cologne around, and was buttoning my shirt when the chimes rang.

That's when I really began to feel the old Christmas spirit, because who should be standing there but those two fellows from the liquor store with my gift from the owner. It was a small green fir tree, but what made it special was the way it had candles instead of bulbs, and a hundred little candy canes for decoration.

I almost panicked when I didn't see any mistletoe, but as soon as I mentioned it, one of the fellows gave a big wink and produced it from inside his jacket. I made a gesture of reaching for a tip, even though I knew I didn't have a dime in my pocket, but they wouldn't hear of it. So we settled for some more Merry Christmases.

After I transferred the Russian vodka to the freezer, I realized I had to have a stand for the tree, because there was that much caviar to put under it. Anyway, it was while I was searching through this box I found in the closet that I came across an oil painting of flowers. But it wasn't until I'd hung it on that barren living-room wall that I saw the tiny initials in the corner—*rh*.

It kind of made me swallow, since it was the only bit of warmth I had found in this stark, impersonal house with its Mrs. Danforth-type housekeeper. And just because Miss Hayworth had painted it, she was too modest to let anyone know, which should tell you something.

I knew the vodka wasn't really cold yet, but I had managed to get the toast, and the hard-boiled eggs, with the whites separated from the yolks, chopped and ready. But most important, I had hung the mistletoe, which she would be under when I had her light the candles on the tree.

Maybe when you get your first glimpse of Miss Hayworth—because if you've never been lucky enough to see her in person, you've never seen her—you'll know what it's like to have your breath sort of catch in your throat.

She was Venus with arms. I mean, when I took a look at the rest of her, which I hadn't really seen because of those old baggy jeans she'd been wearing, I realized all that I had been missing. She not only filled out a blouse to perfection, but she had these gorgeous square shoulders. And with that old towel no longer wrapped around her head, her auburn hair cascaded down around them. She had no hips at all, and even in that tailored skirt, she had those trim, slim legs that told you she had to be an athlete or a dancer. Since I can't stand women athletes, unless they skate, or dive, or play golf, or maybe do the backstroke like Eleanor Holmes, I couldn't have been more pleased that she was a dancer.

She paused halfway down the stairs, and her eyes lit up like you wouldn't believe at the tree and the caviar and the iced vodka in a bucket. But before she had a chance to say anything, let alone join me in a toast with the frosted glasses I had filled, the chimes rang.

I cursed under my breath before I remembered it was Christmas Eve, which made me settle for a little prayer that she would ignore it. But when it sounded again, she moved so quickly to answer it that

I was left rooted to the spot, hoping it wasn't Harry's kid, or old Harry himself, or Harry's wife looking for Harry.

Worse than that, it turned out to be Earl Felton again, who was telling her how he'd overdrawn his account, which had made his business manager so mad he'd cut him off without further funds in spite of the season. Then the liquor-store owner had insisted on being paid immediately, which seemed a little mean-spirited on Christmas Eve.

If there's anything that burns me up, it's someone who drops by without phoning first, especially when all they're hinting at is a hand-out. Apparently Felton wasn't used to too many kindnesses, because the way Miss Hayworth agreed to write him a check without so much as a single question about when he might pay her back caused him to come unhinged. Of course it just might have been helped by all the drinking he'd done, and the way he hated Christmas and all. Anyway, not only did he start shedding real tears, but he launched into the whole story of his shoplifting spree in the liquor store.

In an effort to help him pull himself together, Miss Hayworth had no choice but to offer him some vodka. She even gave him the frosted glass I'd poured for her. Then being so goddamn generous and all, she followed it up with some caviar.

It was while bringing that toasted wedge to his mouth—with the garnish of eggs and everything I had so painstakingly chopped—that he suddenly stopped and stared at it.

"Goddamn caviar!" he exploded. "That's what got me into this money bind in the first place! That goddamn caviar!"

He piled another wedge so high it almost covered the back of his hand, as he explained how it was caviar that had made his liquor bill so staggering. What he found so unfair, he maintained, was that the caviar was one item he had *never* stolen—not to mention one or more quarts of Stolichnaya.

"So some thieving sonofabitch is celebrating the holidays *on me!*" he snarled. "Goddamn caviar!"

I could hardly believe that Miss Hayworth had showed not a hint of suspicion at where the caviar we were eating or the vodka came from. Instead, she was watching Felton with a look of unalloyed concern.

"You've often told me how much it meant to your mother, Earl, that you attend early mass," Miss Hayworth said. "Wouldn't it be a good idea, since tomorrow is Christmas, for you to go and light a candle."

I almost had to laugh at the way old Earl began to fidget, since he still didn't have his check. "Well, after all these years, I don't know," he said. "I wouldn't want to make Mom uneasy in her grave at this late date by being some kind of hypocrite . . ."

"I wasn't thinking just of you, but of whoever stole the caviar, as well," Miss Hayworth said. If she had looked at me then, I don't know what I'd have done. But as I said, she was incapable of that kind of suspicion. "It wouldn't be hypocrisy, Earl. You would be praying for *both* of you."

"Turn the other cheek, that sort of thing," Earl mumbled, looking pained. "Yes, yes, of course . . ." His voice trailed off. Only this time he didn't bother with another caviar wedge, but dropped at a gulp the vodka in my frosted glass—the vodka I'd been saving out of politeness until Miss Hayworth could join me—then pocketed the check she'd handed him and let her show him to the door.

I stood marveling at how in her innocence she had fenced Felton in, then ever-so-subtly closed the gate. First, her mention of his mother, then church, and then the poor misbegotten thief. I couldn't help feeling that if I pointed out to her what she had done, she would almost have had to laugh.

And that's what I was debating, when she returned and discovered her painting that I had hung on the wall. After she got over her embarrassment, I discovered how much her painting meant to her, and the next thing I found myself telling her how much my writing meant to me. So we wound up making a kind of pact—that's how close those unexpected hours had brought us—that one day she'd do nothing but paint, and I'd do nothing but write, and we'd indulge in the luxury of pleasing ourselves before we gave a thought to pleasing others.

I was so caught up by the mood and her nearness, that it took a moment, even though the other lights were out, before I realized we had finished lighting all the candles on the tree, and that she was standing under the mistletoe. Our eyes met in the mirror that ran along the wall, and I could tell she knew where she was standing, too. I figured it was now or never, if I was going to make that mistletoe work for me.

Only before I could make my move, the bells in some church that had struck the hour segued into this very religious music, and she closed her eyes as if she was praying.

I had a bad moment, where I said to myself, she can't be so apprehensive that she's *praying* I won't nail her. But then the music stopped and she opened her eyes.

"I think it's so very selfish the way we always pray for something for ourselves," she said. "So this time I was praying for you."

"Me . . . ?" I said—I was that surprised.

"Yes," she said. "I prayed you would be able to sleep nights."

That was the last thing I expected. "What makes you think I don't?"

She looked startled. "After the way you spend your days?" she said. "I just hope I'm not too late with my prayer."

I was looking into those eyes of hers, and for the first time I noticed among all those flecks of color the humor that was lurking there. I realized she knew *everything*—not just my filching the caviar, but everything, and that included Felton, the employment agency, even the fan at the door.

"I mean with so much on your conscience," she said since I continued to stare, "you *do* find it difficult, don't you?"

"Only when I look back over my day and discover I told a truth, when I could have told a lie," I said, which happened to be the third time since I'd met her for a total honesty on my part.

She sort of cocked her head, weighing that, then I could see those lights returning to her eyes, so I started to join her under the mistletoe, when the chimes sounded.

Before disappearing into the entryway, I paused ever so briefly. "Just don't move," I said, and I underlined each one of those words.

When I swung open the door, I knew I had the answer guaranteed to get rid of anybody—except the one person who was standing there. I recognized him right away from his pictures, and I guess I was so thunderstruck that I don't even remember what I said, if anything.

It was the Prince, and his arms were piled high with gifts, and he was a lot better looking than the papers made him out to be. Although I couldn't see into the living room from the front door, I couldn't help hearing his voice once he had moved past me.

"Candles and caviar!" he cried delightedly. "You *knew* I'd be here! You darling!"

I guess that was what he said, because what I really remember was what I had been working for all day. I heard her laugh.

"You are laughing at me," I heard the Prince say in his precise English.

"No, I'm laughing at what the person said who just opened the door for you, it's that delightful," she said. "Don't ever tell me the truth again, about anything. Promise?"

"You know I cannot lie."

"You can if you want to sleep nights."

She started to laugh again, and that was the last thing I heard, because I closed the door behind me and headed down the walk.

I guess I was walking in circles, because I must have knocked off a couple of miles and still wasn't any nearer home, which made me realize the last thing I wanted was to have to talk to anyone. At least you've got an idea of how rotten I was feeling when I became aware of old Harry coming toward me with his two scotties. I knew he had seen me so there was no way to avoid him, but I made up my mind the one thing I *wasn't* going to talk about was Rita Hayworth. I knew if he said one word, just one, that had some kind of off-color connotation about my being with her, I knew I'd belt him. In spite of his being so old, and short, and having this kid who he didn't even know to let know he loved her—in spite of all that, I just knew I would.

We had covered almost a block, and Harry hadn't said a word. I guess that's what made him different, he was very sensitive to a person's mood. I can't tell you how much I liked him for that, because if it had been me, I would have wanted to know right away about my catastrophe in New York, since it affected him as much as it did me.

"I don't care what they write or say about her, I like her," I said. It just popped out, sort of angrily, after I swore I didn't want to talk about her.

"She likes you," Harry said.

I glanced over at him, but I could see he was really serious. "You think so?"

"She told me."

It's funny how that hit me, because I got to thinking that maybe I shouldn't have walked out like I did, just because the Prince had shown up. Maybe I should have stayed and let her make a choice.

"Did she say anything else?"

"She said she knew you didn't scrub floors for a living," Harry said.

"She really said that, did she?"

"Yes, she really did."

That almost made me smile, thinking about how she'd had to get on her hands and knees to teach me the circular motion. I don't think I ever liked Harry as much as I did right then.

"I really want to thank you for what you said about me," I said.

Old Harry was like me, and Miss Hayworth, too, the way he got kind of embarrassed if you gave him any kind of a compliment. "I said a lot of things," he said, suddenly gruff.

"I mean about me having talent," I said.

"I know what you mean!" Harry snapped. For such a little man, he could get very feisty. When he got like that I always humored him by not saying anything. So we walked quite a way before he spoke again. "Goddammit! I've told you before!" He was still being tough with me. "You're young, your day is around the corner, so don't let it get you down!"

"Maybe if I could see around corners, I wouldn't have blown this one."

"You mean your trip to New York?"

"What did you think I meant?"

Harry just snorted. "Forget it," he said. "If the brass ring had been up for grabs, I would have been upset for you, but it wasn't."

I should have guessed from the conversation that he already knew about my being fired, but I was that surprised. "You kill me, Harry, you truly do," I said. "You knew I blew it."

Harry sort of chuckled. "They sent me a duplicate of the wire they sent you."

It shows you again what Harry was really like, because he had every right to be upset with me when I came by his house that morning, because when I got fired, that meant he had lost out, too.

"Something will turn up, so don't look so worried," Harry said. And then he was waving to me from the door of his house, and I watched him disappear inside.

I don't know why, but I really felt alone. It's funny when you're feeling like that how warm the lights can look in someone else's house. Anyway, I found myself wandering back past her house. Since you couldn't see it from the street, I didn't slow down.

I had one thing on my mind, though, which kept me from being utterly blue. I just knew the Prince would never solve the riddle of what was behind the pain in her eyes, that is if he was even aware of its being there.

PART TWO

PART TWO

I T had been my first trip to Europe, my first look at Paris, and I never stopped marveling at the magic of that city. Of all the hotels I've been in, none exudes the elegance of the Paris Ritz. People seem automatically to lower their voices once they step inside. I even found myself walking with a softer tread. A sudden hush settled over that already subdued atmosphere. Since I didn't speak any French, I was at a loss to identify the source of the whispered excitement, until I caught her name.

Then there she was. She didn't look a day older than when I had last seen her that Christmas Eve at her house. I started counting on my fingers the number of years that had gone by. It took all of one hand.

Since she was rarely off the front pages, I knew she had recently divorced the Prince. Anything else I might have read about her was forgotten in that moment. My only thought was of the times I had fantasized seeing her in just such a setting, where she had no ties, and when I had made a place for myself in her world.

She was all in white, her fur jacket setting off the glory of her shoulder-length auburn hair. She looked as fresh and cool as the morning. No one better personified the name of that hotel and all it had come to stand for.

I watched her start across the lobby. Her glide was as smooth as a championship skater's. In spite of her incredible beauty, it was that easy grace of hers that gave me my biggest thrill at seeing her again.

Of course, I had one thing going that set me apart from all those other rapt fans. I knew I was the only one to whom she had ever taught the fine art of scrubbing. So I was enjoying that secret moment of superiority when she suddenly changed direction and headed straight for me.

I felt a nervousness I wouldn't have believed after all those years. I wondered if I should address her as Princess now she was no longer married to the Prince. And I knew instinctively that I needed something arresting to say to her, something appropriate to my newfound status, something to let her know I was a member in good standing of her world.

Only I couldn't come up with a thing. I truly couldn't. I was looking into those fabulous eyes of hers and I simply forgot everything else. I was as overcome as I was that day she opened her door. It even took a moment for me to realize she had moved past me, as if she had never seen me at all.

Along with just about everyone in that lobby, I followed her out onto the street, and for the first time I became aware of the three men who clustered around the door of the waiting limousine, then joined her inside. In the buzz of conversation around me, I heard enough English to identify them as the Fedeem brothers, who were planning a picture company built around Miss Hayworth as their star. To give a sense of permanency to their undertaking, they were also planning on marrying her.

"You mean she's going to marry all *three* of the bums?" I said, turning to no one in particular. I was that aghast.

Well, I can't tell you the glares I got, because up until then everyone had been swept up in the romance of the unfolding drama that was Miss Hayworth's life. When the limousine pulled away, the people around me waved. I had to smile, because I was waving, too.

I remember saying to myself, *She didn't recognize me, so why not wave her out of my life?* I had the world where I wanted it, so why complicate things?

Yet after all, I did owe my present success to her in a roundabout way. It was some months after her marriage to the Prince. In researching a pilot for a TV series Harry and I were doing, I was spending my mornings in the morgue of the *Los Angeles Times*. I was reviewing the nineteen-forties, and just about every other newspaper or glossy magazine had something about Rita in it. If there was an accompanying picture of her, then no matter how hard I tried to get on with my own work, I'd find myself stopping to read the article.

She appeared on the cover of *Life* magazine for November 10, 1947. It was the fourth time they had used her photograph on the cover, a record equaled only by Franklin D. Roosevelt. In reviewing her career, they made mention that by the year 1945, 6,000 Americans a week were writing her poems and prayers. The following year, a pinup picture of her was pasted to an atomic bomb—a bombshell on the most destructive explosive device science had so far devised.

It was, in fact, astonishing that she had achieved this worldwide following when she'd made so very few pictures. Other than *Cover Girl* and *The Lady from Shanghai*, there was only a small part in *Only Angels Have Wings*. Yet by the year 1946, when *Gilda* premiered, she had become the supreme symbol of the object of man's desire—the "Love Goddess."

Once I finished my research, she faded into the background of my thoughts for a while. Then I came across a spread on her in another glossy magazine. One snapshot in particular caught my eye. What made it so unusual was that there were no people around her. I'd grown so used to seeing her and the Prince surrounded by an entourage, and invariably at some international race meet, that I no longer gave them more than a passing glance. Most of the time there would be members of Europe's wandering royalty, plus the old Aga. Everyone was always dressed to the nines, but no one ever looked as elegant as Rita. She was every inch the Princess.

In this instance, though, someone had caught her with a high-powered lens; she was entirely unaware of being photographed, with a scarf tied turban-style around her head the way it was that first day I met her. And she was painting.

That was what riveted me. We had talked so much about her doing that very thing. She was all alone by a stream in a little wood. The caption said it was a candid shot taken of her on the Prince's horse-breeding farm in Ireland, where she had been relaxing between social engagements.

She had her canvas propped against a tree. On the ground beside her lay a book—a collection of George Bernard Shaw's plays.

I've neglected to mention that at the time we were lighting the candles on that Christmas tree, I'd been telling her all about Shaw, and why she would be absolutely perfect for the female lead in *Arms and the Man*. So I suddenly knew in my heart that this was Rita's way of sending me a message. I was wrong when I said she wasn't aware of the photographer. There were *always* photographers in her life, dogging her heels, hiding and lurking wherever she might be.

So she must have gone out *purposely* that day to paint and to let me know that she was reading Shaw. And not just reading Shaw, but the very play I had mentioned. It couldn't have been more obvious that she was trying to tell me I was still in her thoughts.

I was busting to tell someone about it, but nobody would understand except old Harry, and he was still sore at me for having spent so much time in the morgue. Then I saw a picture of Dorothy Dumont in the sports section. She was Rita's old stand-in, the one who'd led me onto her set and, in effect, changed the course of my life.

In the picture with Dorothy was the black middleweight prizefighter she was going to marry, along with their best man, Guy Train. Since Guy was an old crony, I called him immediately. I was that anxious to get together with Dorothy and talk Rita.

Guy arranged for me to come to the wedding reception. Since Dorothy and I had had a romance when we were in college, she couldn't have been happier to see me. Once I got through listening to why she had fallen for her new husband, it was my turn to tell her all about Rita. I filled her in on the floor-scrubbing imbroglio, but I really got carried away when I got to the significance I saw in that magazine picture—especially in the painting Rita had been doing and the book of Shaw's plays at her side.

I half expected Dorothy to tease me about it, but instead she went very serious. She said she knew Rita had never been interested in wealth, or the international set, or adulation, but the simpler things in life.

"It wasn't the Shaw, or the fact that you brought her back to her painting that won her," Dorothy said. "It was clearly the scrub brush that did it."

Everyone listening had to smile, and I have to admit, while I was smiling, too, I couldn't have felt better. It wasn't until later, when we were back at Guy's, that a conversation took place that turned my whole future around.

"Do you trust Dorothy?" Guy said.

"Implicitly," I said.

"You certainly don't believe you won Rita Hayworth with a scrub brush?"

"No, but Dorothy knew I'd *like* to believe it, so she made my day for me."

Guy shook his head and started muttering, "Now I've heard everything. A person sees a picture of a woman married to another man and he decides she's crazy about him, because she's reading Shaw and painting."

"Don't forget about his once having scrubbed her floors," I reminded him.

"You're as screwy as Dorothy," Guy said, still muttering as he started packing a suitcase. Now he'd done his duties as best man, he'd decided to take a long vacation, and he wasn't leaving any forwarding address. The last thing he did was to hand me a script he'd been working on, and ask me to do him a favor. He wanted me to make sure the script got safely into the hands of Harold Hecht.

As independent companies began taking over from the major studios, the most promising was one formed by Harold Hecht and Burt Lancaster. Their first picture, *The Flame and the Arrow*, starring Burt, had not only been well received by the public, but had gotten fine critical notices as well.

Once I had delivered the script to Harold, he told me that Guy had spoken highly of my talents at story construction. Hecht said he'd like me to join their company in that capacity. So it was that casual conversation with Guy that had led me to Harold, where I wound up with a whole new career.

My initial assignment was *Apache*. I worked with a writer named James Webb. The picture was released under that title starring Burt Lancaster and Jean Peters. I then went on to work with Borden Chase on *His Majesty O'Keefe*, again with Burt in the lead, and then *The*

Kentuckian, which Burt not only starred in, but directed. At that point, I was given my first picture to produce, *Vera Cruz*, starring Burt and Gary Cooper.

So as I said, in a roundabout way Rita was responsible not only for my being in Paris, but for my present affluence. I couldn't get over how she kept crossing my path. Somebody upstairs was obviously determined to tell me something. Even if I should get involved and lose her again, I knew I should be going to her rescue— rescuing her from the brothers Fedeem.

It was at that juncture that Sir Carol Reed arrived—the reason for my being at the Ritz in the first place. Carol had directed *The Fallen Idol*, *Odd Man Out*, and *The Third Man*. All classics. Now he was working with me on the script of the picture I was to produce and he was to direct, *Trapeze*.

Since there was no way I could think beyond my present dilemma with Rita Hayworth, and since Carol only became interested in a conversation if it revolved around pictures, I hit on a plan to get his expert advice.

He had told me he would like us to do another picture together after *Trapeze*, if we could find an intriguing story. So once we were settled over our drinks in Harry's Bar, I told him I had run across a case of mistaken identity. The only problem, it had a nifty first act but didn't know where to go after that.

I was referring to Rita and me, but naturally I didn't use our names. I started in just the way it happened, with the fellow mistaken for a domestic who winds up scrubbing floors, which is how he meets the glamorous movie star. Then I went on to tell him how their paths had crossed earlier, and how that continued to happen—all the way up to the brothers Fedeeem.

We'd had quite a few drinks by then, which really helped, because Carol seemed more than mildly interested. "Rita Hayworth would be good in the part," he said.

I must have described her better than I knew. "What made you think of her?"

Carol shrugged. "She has such interesting eyes."

"Do you know her?"

"No," he said.

Since I hadn't got to the crux of the fellow's problem I pressed on. "You've got to understand," I said, "for the first time in his life the fellow feels he's got the brass ring."

Carol frowned. "He should get a better ring than that, and he should quit fooling around and put it on her finger."

"It's the brass ring he got for defeating life," I explained. "He doesn't want to endanger that by taking on any outside burdens."

Carol chuckled. "Some *burden*." He looked off into the near distance and I could see I'd lost him. "I passed her in the lobby last night. She has the kind of myopia that makes a person nearly blind without their glasses."

"Was she wearing glasses?"

"No," Carol said. "That's what makes her eyes so extraordinarily beautiful."

No wonder she hadn't recognized me. She was blind as a bat without her glasses. I had forgotten back at her house, the way she was always having to put them on, even when she answered the telephone. As if it helped her to see the person at the other end.

I'd never forget the dignified look she assumed, as though the caller could see her, too. She would put her glasses on when the phone rang, and maybe blink once, just to get herself oriented, then she would answer.

No wonder I found her like no other person in the world. So when Carol told me he would like to read the rest of the story, I promised to get it to him. I couldn't have been more grateful for our meeting, but the main thing on my mind right then was getting a campaign underway that would put the old brass ring on Rita Hayworth's finger.

If ever a venture required the oblique approach, it was this one. In searching my mind for the proper accomplice I narrowed the field to Harold Hecht and Burt Lancaster.

First of all, they both had the requisite prestige in the industry. Equally important, they were readily available, both being involved with me in the making of *Trapeze*. And finally, they were the only other people I knew intimately in Paris who spoke English.

Harold Hecht had been a distinguished literary agent before forming the company with Burt. Among Harold's many talents, the one that particularly interested me was his ability to pull the rug out from under a person. It was the subtlety with which he managed this that was impressive, because he invariably won the admiration of the other party even as they were picking themselves up off the floor. That really made me smile when I thought of it in relation to the brothers Fedeem.

On the other hand, Burt never got his exercise that way. When it came to conditioning, he spent most of his time running or working out on the parallel bars. But what set him apart was an aspect of his character I'd discovered on the golf course.

We were at the Riviera Golf Club on the second hole. I had just putted out. But while I was still reaching into the cup for my ball, Burt said, "What did you take?" He always said it with that steely, blue-eyed gaze, the one that could empty out any bar—even the O.K. Corral. Only before I could answer, he told me. "You took an eight."

Now in accomplishing that eight, I had hooked my drive into the trees, then moved deeper into the woods on my next shot, and finally into a trap. The lip on that trap had been so high there was no way to see over it or into it. So after taking three more to get out of there, I had to heft a high wedge over another clump of trees, and found myself on the green. That was the first time we had seen one another since leaving the tee.

Once the other two players in our foursome had arrived on the green, too, I managed a fifty-foot putt. And sunk it. If something congratulatory had been said about that first, I might not have been so engrossed in shaving a stroke off my score while lost in the rough, and another two when I was hidden from view in that trap. Instead, it was only natural to hesitate when I heard, "What did you take?"

That rattled me sufficiently that I decided to knock off only one of those strokes in the trap. But before I was able to total my score, Burt not only told me what it was but ticked off each of the eight shots I had made.

Then he did something even more incredible. He told each of the other two players exactly how many strokes *they* had taken. It never entered my mind to question where he found the time to hit his own ball. Nor did I ever think to question his score. So while I found his performance initially disconcerting, I came to accept it for the act of legerdemain it truly was.

In making my reentry into Rita's life, I wanted her to afford me this type of integrity-through-association. I had left her on a frivolous note—a chance encounter in which I had taken a certain pride in my ability to manipulate the truth. Now I wanted to erase any vestige of that image. So, in essence, I had to get Burt to arrange a meeting for us with her. At that meeting, I had to make sure she put her glasses on, not only so that she would recognize me, but so that she would see the new me-through-association. Then it would be a simple matter to deliver the coup de grace to the brothers Fedeem.

Since I wanted everything to be casual, I sort of set the mood by being real relaxed when I dropped the name of Rita Hayworth in my next conversation with Burt. I said it was a shame to see someone as talented as she was wrecking her career by playing the wrong parts.

Anyone who knows Burt knows he's always helping struggling people—and sometimes even when they're not struggling, but should be. He said he'd been a fan of Rita's ever since he had seen her in *Gilda*, so he felt it might be a beneficial gesture—for her and for his company—if we made her acquaintance.

Then, as he did everything else once he'd made up his mind, he picked up the phone. I mean he didn't call her agent, or her publicity people, or ours to arrange a meeting, but just told the hotel operator who he was, and they put him through.

It was so simple, especially to a confirmed believer in the oblique approach like myself, that it took me a moment to quit marveling at what it was like not only to be a superstar, but to act like one.

I heard him settling on tea instead of cocktails, then she must have asked if he was bringing anyone else, because he said he would like to bring his wife, who was also a fan of hers. I could tell by the look of satisfaction on his face that he had put the perfect wrapper on the conversation, in case she had any doubts about the sincerity of our visit.

It wasn't until after Burt hung up that I realized he hadn't mentioned me by name. He merely said an associate would be with them. So Rita had no idea I would be coming, too. In a sense, I was glad because it would be bound to double her surprise at seeing me again.

She answered the door herself. Burt made the introductions. Rita smiled at Norma, then me, but that was all. Not a flicker of recognition. Although she didn't have her glasses on, I felt sure the mention of my name would strike a chord.

It was just a momentary setback, because a mission like mine was too big not to keep the end results in mind. So I began enjoying my tea, and admiring Burt's canniness in bringing his wife along. If Rita had any thoughts of putting producers like Burt and me in a class with Harry Cohn, Norma dispelled them. It wasn't just her patrician good looks, her stylish taste in clothes and impeccable manners—Norma radiated a warmth which would make anyone feel at ease. Even someone as reserved as Rita.

The only trouble was the afternoon was slipping away, and I hadn't been able to get Rita to put on her glasses. I had heard all about raising children from both Norma and Rita, and I'd heard Burt talk about integrity on the golf course, which he said was as important there as it was on the screen. So I had taken care of my image-by-association and everything. But she still hadn't realized who I was. And this, in spite of all the little ruses I had used—like asking her to write down the special diet she followed when she was dancing in a musical. I remembered reading somewhere that she went on a strict regimen. Only she already had the diet written down, so she just turned the card over to Norma.

I had reached the point where I was ready to get down on my hands and knees and start scrubbing the floors, only without her glasses on, she wouldn't even have picked up on that clue. It was right about then that she told us how she planned to form her own independent production company with the Fedeem brothers, if she could buy her release from Harry Cohn and Columbia.

She went on to say that there was nothing she would like better than to make a picture with Burt. So Burt got this big smile, something he did even better than chinning himself on the parallel bars.

Hearing about her association with the Fedeem brothers from her lips was almost like a death blow. Then it hit me. All the time I'd had the key to getting her to put on her glasses and never knew it.

So while they were discussing the type of property that would best fit their respective talents, I eased myself out of the room and slipped into the bedroom, where I called the operator and asked her to ring the phone in the living room. Then I eased back into the living room, and it was like I had never left. They were still talking about properties, but were leaning towards the notion of a musical. I immediately seconded that.

The telephone rang.

Right away, Rita got her glasses out of her purse, put them on, then blinked in that dignified way that always made me want to smile. After she picked up the phone and said hello, she listened. Then she got a tiny frown on her face and hung up.

"Raphael must be back," she said. "He thinks it's amusing, the way I put on my glasses before I answer the phone, so he sometimes calls from the bedroom, just to see me do it." She had been looking at Norma as she said this. Now she turned to Burt. "That really *is* silly, isn't it?"

I knew it was imperative that I answer before Burt began another of his monologues, since everything depended on her directing that gaze of hers at me. Now that she had her glasses on, that is.

"It's worse. It's dumb," I said. "I don't think I ever heard of anything so dumb."

The way Norma and Burt looked at me, I realized I must have sounded more emphatic than I had intended. Anyway, I forgot their bewilderment because of the way Miss Hayworth stared, studying me. Then her whole face lit up.

"I remember *you*," she said in that soft, soft voice that seemed to quiet the whole of the Place de la Concorde. "You're the guide who showed us Paris."

Then she turned to Norma. "Aly has a house here, so he thought he knew Paris. But he said he only really saw it for the first time when your guide showed it to us." She sort of flicked a hand at me, before turning to Burt. "Now he's showing *you* the city."

Norma looked uncertain. I could see she was about to straighten Miss Hayworth out, but Burt never paused for breath, he was enjoying the moment that much.

"We've been equally impressed," Burt said. "That's why I signed him to work on the picture we're making."

"Of course. You said you were bringing an associate," she said. And she said it like there was no longer a doubt in her mind about me.

"Yes, he's been spotting locations, that sort of thing," Burt went on. "In fact, he found the Cirque d'Hiver for us."

"I never knew they had lost it," this voice said in a heavy accent. It belonged to the oldest Fedeem brother, the one she called Raphael, who came into the room as though he owned it. He had the dark, sinister looks I've never trusted. It made me realize more than ever the seriousness of the situation she had gotten herself into.

Even though we were standing, I never bothered to shake his hand when she introduced us; I just nodded and started to leave. But when I got to the door, I had a sensation she was watching me, so I paused and glanced back.

I swear she looked like she was going to burst out laughing. I didn't have any idea what that meant, but I had the feeling I had to say something more.

"I also found the Eiffel Tower," I told her, "if you're interested."

Then I headed down the hall to catch up with Norma and Burt.

"I liked her," Norma said.

We had gone directly to Harry's Bar and ordered martinis. I was still so disconcerted I emptied mine at a gulp, but Burt was relishing his.

"I liked her, too," Burt said. "I'm glad we had the meeting."

He caught the cloud on my face and the empty martini glass in front of me and was quick to order another round.

"I'm glad no one spoke up when she mistook you for a guide," he added. "Rita's so shy, it could have been very embarrassing for her." I could see the glint in his eyes again, so I knew he was back to enjoying the situation. "Don't you think so, Norma?" Burt turned to his wife. "The way he let it pass, I was proud of him. He's a real company man."

"I'd have to agree with that," Norma said.

"Damned hard to find, too. A real company man. Not like finding the Cirque d'Hiver, even though that Fedeem fellow never knew it was lost." Burt really laughed at that, before downing his drink. "It's a shame Hill's so rigid in his outlook on marriage."

"How's that?" Norma said.

"If he wasn't so prejudiced, he could rescue her from that Fedeem fellow," Burt said. "I'm sure Hill could do a better job of bringing her out of her shell."

"Why don't you?" Norma said.

There was another problem of having Burt as a friend—one I didn't want to get into with Norma right there. I mean not only could he remember your every stroke on the golf course, but just about everything you said off it.

Now while it was true I had mentioned that anyone who didn't marry a virgin might as well pick his wife out of a whorehouse if he was all that anxious to deal in used goods, I had forgotten I'd said it. But that didn't mean I hadn't meant it. And Burt knew that. So what with his having been married before, and I wasn't sure whether Norma hadn't, too—and the whole world knew about Rita—it could have been a very touchy subject.

"I mean it," Norma persisted. "You should think about marriage."

"I don't know," I said, pretending total disinterest.

"With his hangups, there's no way," Burt said to his wife. "You can't have everything in one person, Norma. And, like we said, Hill's one good company man."

As I lay awake that night, eyeballing the ornate ceiling of my room and reviewing every detail of our visit to Rita, I read everything into it but the one thing that should have registered. I'd forgotten how thoroughly she had fooled me with her apparent naiveté that Christmas Eve at her house. It had come as such a surprise when I discovered not just that she knew everything that had gone on, but that she'd really enjoyed letting me know she knew.

Suddenly I was back to the moment that afternoon when I had turned at the door and said, "I also found the Eiffel Tower, if you're interested." It wasn't what I said that was important, but she had that same mischievous look in those fabulous eyes.

That was when it hit me. She had known who I was all along and it was her way of having fun at my expense. If I was right, and I was

sure I was, then why was she kidding me? And what was she trying
to tell me?

If it hadn't been for the hour, I would have called her right then.
But the clock said it was after four A.M., so I got back under the
covers and this time I went to sleep.

As soon as the stores opened the next morning, I outfitted myself
like a domestic. I even bought a scrub brush and bucket. Only inside
the bucket, I had two five-pound tins of caviar and a quart of that
Russian vodka.

No one said a word when I came through the service entrance at
the Ritz. I had already figured that if anyone questioned me, I'd tell
them I was on my way up to see Sir Carol Reed who was casting the
role of a domestic for the picture he was shooting. The one thing I
didn't want to do was to tip Rita off until I knocked at her door.

I was about to step into the service elevator with some other maids
and valets, when word came that Miss Hayworth was on her way
down. It was like that other morning, the way everybody moved
toward the lobby and an expectant hush settled over the place. The
only difference was that this time she was wearing her glasses.

I wasn't aware of stepping as far into the lobby as I had, but the
next thing I knew she was coming right toward me. This time, she
paused.

"You're a man of surprises," she said. "You're a guide, then you're
a picture maker—*now* what are you up to?"

"I'm back to scrubbing floors and handing out caviar," I said. I
reached into the bucket and came up with a tin. "Remind you of
anything?"

"Yes," she said. "How very much I like caviar."

That was all. Not a trace of recognition, nor a glint in her eyes that
said she recalled our Christmas Eve. Then the Fedeem brothers, who
had been hovering around, began reminding her of the hour and that
they were already late for their plane.

I was probably kidding myself, but I thought she lingered an extra
moment—a moment while we just looked at each other—then she let
them draw her away.

"Smooth flying," I called after her, but she didn't turn back. I
continued to watch her all the way onto the street. I was thinking,

maybe I should have been more specific about the caviar. But if I had, and she still hadn't remembered, I somehow felt I would have lost her for good.

Anyway, that's what I was thinking when who should enter the lobby but Sir Carol Reed. What I loved about Carol was the way he was always oblivious to everything but his picture-making. He took no notice of my outfit or the bucket and scrub brush in my hand.

"I just saw Rita on her way out," he said. "It reminded me of that curious love story you told. You were going to get the rest of it over to me."

"I couldn't find it."

"Why don't you just put down what you remember?"

It was on the tip of my tongue to tell him the truth—that I had really been telling him the story of Rita and me. But after our most recent near miss, I was stuck for the next chapter. Instead, I handed Carol the bucket with the tins of caviar and the vodka.

"I was in Fauchon," I told him, "and it made me think of your wife."

Just like he never noticed my get-up, he never questioned why I would make a present of caviar and Russian vodka in a bucket, or that, in fact, I had never met his wife.

"She'll be terribly pleased," he said. "She loves caviar."

In the weeks that followed, Rita never returned to Paris. Since I was tied up with the shooting of *Trapeze*, there was no way I could leave the city. So every time I picked up a newspaper, I expected to read of her coming marriage, particularly since no matter what part of the world she was photographed in she'd have one of those Fedeem brothers lurking in the background.

I began to see them in my sleep, when who should show up but a contingent of executives from United Artists, headed by their president, Arthur Krim. Since they were financing *Trapeze*, and would also be distributing the picture, I saw a great deal of them, both on and off the set.

It was over drinks with Arthur and one of their top publicists, a man named Fran Winnikus, that I casually inquired about the Fedeems. Arthur said they were discussing a deal to star Rita in a picture, if they could make some kind of arrangement for her services with Harry Cohn and Columbia.

Naturally, I didn't tell Arthur I had a personal interest in Miss Hayworth. But I did tell him that Burt and I had spent an afternoon with her, and we had talked about making a picture together. I told Arthur I didn't want to get Burt too involved until we knew something could be worked out on Miss Hayworth's part. So what I suggested instead was an informal meeting—just him and Rita and me. Somewhere that would appear almost accidental, like the party we were giving in New York following the premiere of *Trapeze*.

Arthur frowned, as if that was making a business meeting *too* informal, but Fran Winnikus spoke up. He said he happened to know that Rita was going to New York at that time and it would be a big publicity coup for the movie to have her there.

After Arthur left us, I reemphasized to Fran how important it was to make everything appear accidental, so that Miss Hayworth wouldn't think we were ganging up on her, or resorting to the sort of underhanded tactics of the brothers Fedeem. I also told Fran it might not hurt my credibility with Rita if he had Arthur Krim point out my not being married. Just so she wouldn't think anything funny was going on—any married-producer hijinks reminiscent of her encounters with Harry Cohn.

Then I got confidential with Fran. I told him I couldn't divulge the plot of the movie I had in mind for Rita because it would be too easy to steal, but the whole publicizing of the venture depended on her *not* being married. Fran said he didn't see how he could guarantee such a thing, especially with someone like Rita. I told him it was only important that she still be single when I ran into her accidentally at the premiere party. After that, I said, it would be up to me to keep her that way.

Since Fran's whole life was built around publicity, he said he would check out that aspect of Rita's life as soon as he returned to New York. It was about a week later that I got a cable from Fran. He said that everything was set for my "accidental" meeting with Rita, and far more important, she had assured him she wouldn't be married before then.

The news contained in that cable stayed with me right through the final days of the shooting on *Trapeze*.

I've never felt a picture was really over until I've boarded the plane for the States. Burt's wife, Norma, had gone on ahead to get their children settled in school. That meant we'd be traveling together from Paris to London, where we had to spend a couple of days before taking off on the flight to New York.

It wasn't until we were on the New York plane that the euphoria started setting in. It was as though I was high on martinis before I even had one. And I wasn't alone in this. Of all the people involved in the making of a movie, the performers are under the most constant stress. So it was nice to see Burt begin to relax with a martini.

I figured I would wait until we'd had at least a couple before getting down to business. That gave the stewardess and everyone seated around us a chance to get over their initial wonder at having a movie star in their midst.

Anyway, we had mellowed into a fresh martini when I said, "I've decided to do something about my image."

"You think that's possible?"

"Don't you?"

Burt looked thoughtful, took a pull on his martini, then brightened. "You're going to shoot yourself."

"Why should I shoot myself?"

"Is there any alternative?"

Now *I* brightened. "Marriage."

Burt sighed. "Who are you planning on dragging down to your level? Anyone I know?" he finally said.

"You've met her."

"Let me guess."

"No," I said. "I'd rather you knew who she was for the first time when we're at the party after the premiere in New York."

I wanted to be specific, but not that specific. I figured if he knew ahead of time, he might bump into her unexpectedly and start congratulating her before she knew why.

"If you don't tell me who she is," he said, "how will I know?"

"I'll be dancing with her," I said. "I'll dance every dance with her. So no matter what time you arrive at the party, you'll know who she is."

"You must really like her," he said, "if you're going to dance that much."

I grinned at that, while he caught the stewardess's eye for another martini. The conversation had finally arrived at the point where I'd been steering it right along.

"I don't intend to dance with anyone else ever again. That's how much I like her," I said as the drinks arrived. "But that doesn't mean you can't cut in."

Then I went on to tell him the part he played in my strategy— how I'd like him to mention what a swell, erudite fellow I was, besides being true blue in my relationships, and devoted to my parents and other minorities, and how I wrote all the pictures we made, but never bothered to take the credit. Little things like that.

Burt slowly turned his head to me. He appeared that shocked. "You mean you want me to *lie*."

Since being an actor meant never being yourself but somebody else, I would have thought lying would have been second nature. Yet in all the time I had known Burt, I had never heard him tell a lie. At least none I'd caught him in.

So I made it clear that I didn't want him to start now. If he felt I was overdoing it, then I told him to forget about the minorities bit, which tells something about how many martinis I'd had. Because that was the only part I felt I might not have been absolutely truthful about.

Somehow, that made him laugh. "Okay, I'll do it," he said. "Anything to get you off the streets."

Those words were like handing me the key that could lock up the whole situation with Rita and brought us to the beautiful part. We clinked glasses, but they were the cheap kind and they broke. So after the stewardess cleaned up the mess, with a lot more toweling where it really wasn't necessary, we got fresh martinis. But we didn't risk clinking again. Instead, we settled on a handshake. And that's what I meant about the beauty part, because we realized we had never shaken hands before.

We probably had never even been *introduced*. It was really something, finally to meet after all we'd been through together. I was moved. Truly I was. Never have I wanted so much to do something for another person. It wasn't the martinis, either—I swear it—although I changed the next round to doubles, more to stimulate my thinking than anything else. It was well nigh impossible to come up with a gift for a superstar. I mean when you talk about someone who has everything, including the ability to walk around on his fingertips, that's Burt. Then, with a real gulp from the old double, it suddenly hit me.

Burt told me how he had been to college, but I noticed he never talked about being a member of a fraternity, which meant he had lost out on the only reason for going in the first place. So I gave him our secret fraternity handshake, after having him take an oath that he'd never reveal it. I told him if he was ever in Seattle and broke—and especially if it was raining—he could always use it for a free meal at the Phi Gamma Delta fraternity.

Naturally, we drank to that, and practiced the grip, of course, and had another, and I told him the Latin password that would ensure the wearing of a robe and a roof over his head, and I guess we had another, and maybe another, and someplace along the line we knocked down three rows of seats, including the ones we had been sitting in.

Everyone from the cockpit came hurrying back to investigate the chaos, which clearly upset Burt because his eyes and his voice went ice cold, like when he was Sergeant Warden in *From Here to Eternity*, and there was a war to be fought.

"Shouldn't somebody be up front flying this thing!"

Well, they all scrambled back up front to their flying business and at that moment a dignified, white-haired gentleman, who turned out to be Artur Rubinstein, leaned over to us.

"For a moment there, I thought I'd miss my next concert," Mister Rubinstein said in this real appreciative voice. I mean he was that grateful to Burt for getting those flying aces back to their seats in the cockpit. Then the stewardess straightened up from someplace on the floor, or wherever she'd been hiding.

"Are you two all right?" she said.

"We will be once you get us a couple of fresh martinis," Burt said before settling back and turning to me. "Now, where were we?"

"You were going to cut in on the girl I'll be dancing with—"

"Yes, yes"—he interrupted, again smiling that foxy smile to himself—"and tell her some lies—."

Burt's wife had flown into New York from the coast, so I knew I wouldn't be seeing him again until the night of the premiere. I was having lunch at Lindy's with Bernie Kamber, who, as head of our publicity department, was in charge of all the arrangements. There were any number of details I wanted to go over with Bernie at the opportune time but, like Burt, I didn't want him privy to my plans for Rita Hayworth.

I really enjoyed Bernie. He was always telling jokes without punch lines. You could burst out laughing any old time, even if he hadn't said anything. Bernie would figure you had finally gotten the tag of the joke you hadn't laughed at yesterday.

"Finally figured it out, did you?" Bernie would say, with this real satisfied look, and then he'd start laughing. Bernie had these false teeth that were always on the move, even when he wasn't talking. I thought of them as his roving crockery. But outside of Burt, he had the vital answers to so many of the things that lay ahead—like the music the orchestra would be playing, which was what we were going over at the moment.

I figured the one way to get Rita away from the Fedeem brothers, if she should have them in tow, was to get her out on the dance floor. So I was subtly getting across to Bernie how nice it would be for the squares—which included all the United Artists brass—if they played a lot of waltzes. That's about the only dance I can do, when I want to talk a lot and not have to worry about keeping time to the music, too.

We were eating Lindy's famous pastrami sandwiches at the time, and Bernie started comparing our company to them. "You're like a sandwich without any filling, Hill," Bernie said, and his crockery was roving something fierce, like it did when he was on a real serious kick. "Take this one slice of rye. Think of it as Hecht. Then there's the other slice, which is Lancaster. Everybody's heard of Hecht.

Everybody's heard of Lancaster. But you're in the middle and *nobody's* ever heard of you. We don't come to Lindy's to get a sandwich with nothing in between the rye."

"I understand about Lancaster," I said, "but who has ever heard of Hecht?"

"They think he's *Ben* Hecht," Bernie said. "He couldn't be better known."

It had never occurred to me that everybody would think of Harold as Ben Hecht, who just happened to be the foremost writer in the business. It gave me a whole new feeling of admiration for old Harold.

"I see," I finally said, and I was getting this empty feeling, because I really did.

"We've got to get you *known*," Bernie said. "Otherwise, I can't get space on you. I'm wasting my time. I've tried to think of some well-known author, so we can let the public think you're him. But the two don't seem to go together."

"You mean no one who can write has my name?" I said, feeling even lower.

"Exactly," Bernie said.

"There was a famous James Hill who built the Great Northern Railroad," I said, even though I knew he had never written anything.

"Recently?"

"Middle of the last century," I said. "In grammar school, teachers were always asking me if he was a relative."

"Nobody rides the trains anymore," Bernie said. "If he had come up with the plane that broke the sound barrier, *then* we might have something—especially if he'd also written a hit play."

Bernie lit up a cigar then, which meant he was going to let the crockery rest for a spell. So somehow it didn't seem good manners to engage in any more conversation. I can't tell you how depressed I was feeling, because who wants a sandwich without any filling. No wonder Rita pretended not to know me. After all, she'd been married to Orson Welles and then Aly Khan, so unless I could justify my place alongside them, I didn't deserve her recognition. That was when it hit me.

If I married her, or even had my name linked with hers, I'd be headline news. But if she fell in love with me for that, I wouldn't want it. If she couldn't accept me for myself, then I'd have to pass. The whole ridiculousness of her falling in love with me because I had become famous by marrying her got me to laughing out loud. It's tough to stay serious when you're into this kind of complicated courting.

Naturally, Bernie thought I'd figured out one of his jokes, so he started laughing, too. While he was in such a good mood, I got him to agree to have the orchestra make every other dance a waltz.

I walked Bernie back to his office, which was in the same building as Arthur Krim and United Artists. I knew he would insist I say hello to Arthur as long as I was in the building, which was exactly my intent. I just didn't want Arthur to think I had made a special trip to see him, because money men can be very wary.

So once Bernie told a couple of jokes, he left me alone with Arthur, who right away asked what I thought Burt would be doing now *Trapeze* was behind him. I said I had a story in mind for him and Rita Hayworth, but there were certain unresolved questions in my mind.

"I'm kind of disturbed about her memory, for one thing, Arthur," I said. "If anything drives Burt up the wall, it's someone who has a lousy memory."

"You mean," Arthur Krim said, "like remembering her lines?"

"It could get to that," I said.

"She has a reputation for being a strict disciplinarian once she commits herself to a project."

"I guess what made me worry was this one incident," I said. "When I saw her in Paris with Burt and his wife, she said she remembered an earlier meeting of ours—only she remembered me as the guide who had shown her and the Prince the city. Well, I've never been a guide. Not even at Radio City Music Hall. I was a page there, but never a guide. So you see, if her memory's that bad, the next thing she'll be forgetting her lines, or something worse, and Burt'll really be up the wall."

Arthur started chuckling, and I realized what I liked about him, besides his reassuring laugh, was that he hadn't let his hair grow all over the place in the back just because it was receding in the front.

"She told me about that," he said. "She realized later what a mistake she had made."

I tried not to let my excitement show. "Then she remembered our first meeting."

"Yes, and that's why she felt so badly," Arthur said. "She said she must have gotten her husbands mixed up."

"Her husbands . . . ?"

"Orson and Aly," Arthur said. "It was Orson she was with when she first met you, not Aly. She remembered how you kept the saws sharp for his magic act."

I could hardly believe my ears, I was that staggered. "*I* kept the saws sharp . . . !"

"In Las Vegas. She couldn't get over how well you did the job," Arthur Krim said. "In all the times Orson sawed her in half, she said she never once felt a thing."

I had to pull myself together, despite the fact that I felt deeply let down. If you want to get financing for another picture, it's unwise to show this sort of weakness around the backer. So I told Krim how much I appreciated his clearing up the matter of her memory, only there was one other point that Burt found even touchier.

"He hates working with people who have no sense of humor," I said. "Does she joke a lot?"

Arthur frowned, like I had mentioned dirty jokes or something. "*Joke* a lot . . . ?"

"You know, like me sharpening the saws," I said. "Would she joke about something like that?"

Arthur began looking at me kind of funny, which made me all the more aware of how his hair was in fact receding, and it was getting a little long in the back, too.

"When you're as beautiful and talented as Rita Hayworth," Arthur said, "you don't have to joke."

"What I really mean is, does she have a sense of humor?"

"With the world at her feet, why would she need one?"

"I guess what I'm trying to say is do you think she'll marry the Fedeem brothers?" I said. Well, the way Arthur Krim looked at me this time, I knew I'd better say something more. "I suppose that really would take a sense of humor, from what I've seen of them."

Arthur Krim's face got as frosty as if he had just come out of a freezer, which wasn't too surprising, now that I remembered that his company was financing the Fedeem brothers' next picture.

"Burt's not worried about her personal life, too?" Arthur Krim said, and his voice was caustic.

"Well, you know Burt, he's such a perfectionist."

"Miss Hayworth would never let that part of her life affect her work," Arthur Krim said.

I could feel I was running out of ammunition, which I think Arthur was also feeling. Then I remembered that he lived with his mother, or used to, or was very close to her, or something.

"I've never told this to anyone, Arthur," I said, lowering my voice confidentially, "but I think Burt's success was due entirely to his mother. I live with my mother, so I have a special hunch about such things. I mean, that's what was really behind my whole conversation."

At first that seemed to confuse him—the part about what was behind my conversation—then it all suddenly rang a bell and his whole face softened. I knew he was thinking of his own mother.

"I have the greatest respect for Burt," he said, and he even confirmed it with a nod or two.

"I'm not that close to Rita," I said, "so I don't know how she feels about me, or her mother."

Arthur fastened his gaze on me. I could tell he was seeing me in a new light. "I'm sure she was very fond of her mother," he said. "I can also say she liked you."

"You could tell?"

"She said as much when I mentioned your name," Arthur said. "And when I brought up the party, she immediately said she'd be glad to attend."

"It'll be a chance to get her together again with Burt," I said.

"I'm sure once you decide on a subject, you'll have a fine picture with the two of them."

Well, Arthur Krim looked like he'd just stepped out of the barber's chair at the Waldorf. It wasn't just because he had verified that Rita would be at the party. Or that she liked me. I only knew I couldn't have wanted to see his hair any other way, but receding a little, and very neat in the back. The way he was wearing it as I left his office.

If ever I felt in a mood to conquer, it was when I walked into the party after the premiere of *Trapeze*. I had picked up an orchid, which I had pinned to the lapel of my tuxedo. I was planning on letting Rita wear it in her hair.

Bernie was waiting for me at the bar with a girl who had once sat beside me at a dinner party. So though we had met before, it never entered my mind to greet her with more than a polite smile. I mean I was already feeling that much out of circulation—which showed how far I was getting ahead of myself—since the girl happened to be a well-known personality. I almost said actress, but I've never seen too much acting when someone has her kind of chest on display.

We took our drinks from the bar to a table, where everyone's name was on a card, with Jayne's right next to mine. All the while Bernie was telling me sotto voce how much she had wanted to be seated next to me for the evening, which was the reason she had broken a date in the first place. And Jayne kept giving little squeals of delight.

"I guess we'll have a little something to put between those two slices of bread after tonight," Bernie said, his eyes rolling suggestively from Jayne to me. "I can already see Earl Wilson looking over here."

"I'm crazy about him," Jayne kept saying.

I might have been more impressed by her flattery, but with each breathless word the lone button that held the top of her dress together would quiver under the terrific strain. And when she burst into laughter, like she did every moment or two, it would disappear, then bob back up again.

"He has to be the funniest man I ever met, Bernie," she said after pausing to catch her breath. "I really am crazy about him."

I hadn't said a word, except maybe swallowed a little too loud from sheer terror, and I was the funniest. Imagine the fate of that button if I actually said something.

The first person I thought of trading places with was Joe Di-Maggio. If anyone could catch whatever went into orbit when that button gave, it had to be Joe. He was seated at the next table, so it was just a matter of telling him that Jayne couldn't stop talking about him and his 56-game hitting streak.

Only before I could make a move, the button went. I hadn't said anything to provoke it, and she hadn't even laughed. About all I could do was glance around for help, but I discovered I was alone at the table with Jayne. I'd been so nervous, I'd been unaware of Bernie leaving to go over to talk to Earl Wilson.

It was a desperate moment, because all I could think of, while I was on my knees running the button down, was Arthur Krim bringing Rita over. Once I trapped the button on the floor and straightened up, there was still no sign of them, so I went about the job of helping Jayne get it back in place.

I won't go into details, but it was like the Mae West hole at the Bel-Air Golf Course, where you can't see the flag on the other side for these two enormous mounds. So you have to hit a blind shot between them and pray.

I had my eyes closed in prayer for what seemed like an hour, before Jayne, who was using both hands to hold the top of her dress together, finally said I had found the hole, or whatever the button snapped into. I was almost afraid to open my eyes, but fortunately there was still no sign of Rita.

"I was crazy about you before," Jayne said in her breathless way, "because I thought you were the funniest person I had ever met. But I never thought I could fall in love with you."

"I was just lucky with that button," I said modestly, since I couldn't believe she was serious. "It's like the Mae West hole at Bel-Air. Some days you can't get close to the hole, no matter how hard you try."

"I don't know about that, but I know I trust you," she said. "The only other person I've ever trusted was my father."

"What about your husband?"

"The one I just divorced?" she said. "I had two kids before I realized I couldn't trust him."

That was when I knew she was serious, because I could see her eyes had misted over. I know it sounds crazy, but I was genuinely touched.

"You know what I'd like to do?" she said. And she smiled. "I'd like to dance with someone I really trust."

I was proud of the way I didn't hesitate, not even to down the rest of my martini. And in spite of not wanting to leave that table so I could keep an eye out for Rita, I made my way out onto the dance floor with Jayne. I sort of felt like a boy scout who was doing his good deed.

It was in the midst of that warm glow that I saw Rita coming in with Arthur Krim. While I was figuring how best to extricate myself from Jayne, she informed me that the button was about to go again. I had visions of everything emerging right there on the dance floor, with photographers snapping all over the place.

"If the button's about to go," I managed, "then perhaps you had better try for the lady's room, where they can help you fix it."

"No, that's not necessary," Jayne said. "Nothing can happen as long as we dance real close."

We were already practically dancing as one, but now she moved even closer and I began picturing our return to the table, where Arthur would be waiting for Rita. I could see myself stepping back to shake hands and Jayne revealed in all her glory. Panic possessed me.

"May I cut in?" a familiar voice said.

It was Burt. Never in my life have I been so glad to see anyone. As soon as I had made the introductions, I slid Jayne into his arms, which kept her pressed against my chest and then his. She was so excited at meeting Burt that I could tell she had forgotten about the button.

"She likes to dance close, the way all good dancers do," I said. "Isn't that right, Jayne?"

"If I enjoy someone, yes," she said, snuggling up to Burt. I could tell by the smile she gave me that she had gotten the message.

When I returned to my table, there were Rita and Arthur Krim. And, for the moment, there were no Fedeem brothers. Once we had shaken hands, Arthur said how much the audience had enjoyed the picture, which made me feel terrific. I mean it identified me right away to Rita as one of the producers, so that this time there was no way she could take me for someone else.

Then the orchestra moved into a waltz. Right away, Arthur said that sounded like our kind of music, meaning Rita and me. I needed no more cue than that to lead her onto the dance floor. I had a dark corner picked out, where we would be cut off from the rest of the crowd. On my way to it, I gave Arthur an appreciative wave over Rita's lovely shoulder.

I swear it was like holding air. I never felt a thing dancing with her. Once we got to that secluded corner, I paused long enough to give her the orchid. She had some kind of jeweled pin in her hair, so she used that to fasten it in place.

"No caviar?" she said.

I had to smile, because she hadn't forgotten the last time, when I handed her the tin of caviar as she was leaving the Ritz. I was hoping she might have figured out in the meantime why I had given it to her, but when she didn't elaborate, I resolved not to waste any more time.

"I've run across a story that could be perfect for you," I said.

"I was wondering which of your hats you'd be wearing tonight," she said. "You're a moviemaker."

"Only because I told the story to Sir Carol Reed, who thought of you immediately."

"I'm a big fan of his."

"He feels the same about you," I said. "That was why I was so anxious to see you tonight and get your reaction."

Then I started at the beginning with Harry and his kid and the return of the Christmas present. I didn't leave out a detail, because I figured she *had* to recognize herself, and then me. Once I had accomplished that, I was confident I would have the evening in the palm of my hand, because of the ending I had in mind for the story.

Only I had gotten no further than the point where she had taken me for someone from the employment agency, when she frowned. I could tell something was bothering her, so rather than continue I used the moment to check on my dancing. We were still in that secluded spot, and they were still playing the waltz, and—equally encouraging—I was still in time.

"But would a movie star take in someone to scrub her floors, even if she thought he was from the employment agency?" she said. "Wouldn't she insist on seeing his credentials?"

I was so sure her frown had been provoked by her dawning recognition of the two characters that I was a moment in answering.

"You've said exactly what was going through her mind as she showed him how to use the scrub brush. But he caught on so quickly —and she was so desperate to get the work done, what with its being Christmas Eve—she decided to overlook that fact."

When Arthur Krim had told me how very thorough she was when it came to her work, he had been understating. I've never told a story where every incident was examined with such a fine-tooth comb. I couldn't help feeling she must be pulling my leg. But she seemed so sincere, I simply couldn't risk challenging her on that point.

Anyway, when I finally got to the end—where the movie star gives up her whole career to paint—she lost her frown for the first time. "I like her doing that," she said, "but I wonder if I could play someone that brave?"

"You paint. I saw a newspaper picture of you painting," I said. "So it must have passed through your mind."

"I can't tell you how many times," she said. "And what about the man? Does he become a writer?"

"That's what she does for him," I said. "When she walks away, he decides to walk away, too."

Her eyes lit up. All the flecks of green and gold started dancing in them.

"I like it," she said. "I really like it."

I was so excited I did a couple of tricky little steps, since there wasn't anything I could do that she couldn't follow. I remembered her dancing with Gene Kelly in *Cover Girl*. With a partner like Rita, he couldn't help being great.

There was scattered applause from a small group that had gathered around us, but the only ones I was really aware of were the three Fedeem brothers. Naturally, I took for granted the clapping was a tribute to Miss Hayworth and those tricky steps I had done. Then I became aware that the orchestra wasn't playing.

Somehow I couldn't make myself stop. Instead, I sort of petered

out, like a clock that needs winding. It made everyone
chuckle, but best of all, Rita looked up at me with this big smile.
"I had no idea the music had stopped," she said. Then she turned
to the oldest Fedeem. "I just had no idea."

"If he's that good without music, think how good he'll be with the
orchestra playing," the eldest Fedeem said. But it didn't even draw a
laugh.

I felt sorry for him. I truly did. I had come to conquer, and I had.
There was nothing he could say that would change the way Rita was
looking at me.

I was about to ask her if she wanted to wait for the music—or
would she care to dance again without it—just to rub it in, when
Burt showed up, kind of out of breath.

"I've *never* told so many lies, but she's yours. All yours," he said.
"I don't know what she'll be wearing for the wedding, but when I
told her how much it meant to you to marry her, she stepped back
and she was practically naked. But she was too excited to care. Congratulations! She's all yours now. For better or for worse!"

He started pumping my hand, but the only thing I was aware of
were those eyes of Rita's. They had a bewildered look, as she turned
from Burt to me. If ever I was desperate for words, it was right then.
But before I could think of anything, Burt discovered her.

"I've never played cupid before, but I think it's all for the best," he
explained to Rita. "Once he's married, it will make him more accept-
able to our wives, which is bound to make him a better company
man."

Rita seemed to need a moment to digest that, then she stepped
forward and held out her hand.

"Congratulations," she said.

I took her hand in mine, and while I still couldn't think of anything
to say, I just knew I never wanted to let it go. Only in that terrible
moment, the Fedeem brothers had come back into their own and,
before I knew it, they were leading her away.

I suddenly found my voice. "Wait!" I cried, as I watched her
disappear into the crowd.

I started after her, when Burt hooked a finger into the back of my
collar and brought me to an abrupt halt.

"You can't run away now," Burt said.

"I wasn't," I managed to gasp. "I just wanted to explain something to Rita."

"You've got to forget about Rita and all the other girls you've known," Burt said, still grasping me firmly by the back of my collar. "This is what it *means* to get married—you'd better get used to the idea of one girl starting now!"

That was when the button popped on my collar. I had been straining so hard, I nearly felt flat on my face, but I managed to catch myself. It was getting to be a night for popping buttons, but right then I was only interested in tracking Rita down. So I headed in the direction in which she'd vanished.

The orchid was lying right by the front door, which told me it had been thrown aside on her way out. She hadn't even bothered to take out the jeweled pin that had fastened it in her hair.

At first, I tried to tell myself it was the eldest Fedeem who had torn it from her head and flung it away, then trampled it in terrible jealousy. So my first instinct had been to go charging out into the night and rescue her. Only I knew I had to gulp a double martini first, and that's when I began to realize my lies were catching up to me.

I'm not saying other people didn't believe them, but *I* was beginning not to believe them. First of all, the orchid still looked as fresh as when I had filched it in the florist shop while old Burt had been buying a corsage for his wife, which meant no one had torn it from her head. Instead, she, herself, had cast it away. Second, if I was going to rescue her, what was I rescuing her from.

I mean, here was this great beauty with the nifty glide, who had walked away not just from a prince, but one who was the son of the richest man in the world, one who had the finest racing stable around, and who was good-looking besides—something I rarely admitted about the competition. Now if they hadn't satisfied her, then what was she after? Who was I to be rescuing her? And from what?

I had ducked into a bar off the entrance, and that was when the first tear came. It plopped right down into my empty martini glass, alerting me that I had just finished gulping my double. I limited myself to one more, which made it possible to pull myself together and return to Burt. He gave me one of his icier glares, but before he could say anything, I spoke first.

"Where's Jayne?" I said.

"She's bringing over her godfather, the ex-mayor of New York," Burt said. He had a martini in his hand, which he downed then smiled as though innocent of the terrible wrong he had done me. "She wants him to get together with us and arrange the wedding."

"I've got to make you understand one thing before they get here," I told him. "I never planned on Jayne's being my partner when you cut in."

Burt bared his teeth in a chuckle. "Frankly, I was surprised myself," he said. "I had a hunch it would be Rita Hayworth."

I grasped the lapels of his tuxedo. "You've got to help me!" I cried. "We're on the verge of a terrible mistake that could wreck my whole future!"

Then I laid it all out, from scrubbing the floors that day at her house, to our meeting at the Ritz with Norma, and finally, his mistaking Jayne for my intended. I don't know how I managed to get so much in, because we had only finished two more doubles—which made everything *else* seem double—when I heard a familiar squeal.

Jayne had a fur stole wrapped around her shoulders and her godfather on her arm. The ex-mayor told Burt how appropriate he thought it would be if we chartered a ferry to the Statue of Liberty for the wedding party, then held the marriage itself up in the torch, where he'd be glad to perform the ceremony.

"You're qualified, are you?" Burt said in his real stern Nuremberg voice.

"Ordained," the ex-mayor said. "You have to have something to fall back on."

It was this kind of probing on Burt's part that not only gave such depth to his acting, but gave me real confidence in the ultimate outcome of this miserable misadventure.

"I'm sure everyone knows how patriotic Jayne is," the ex-mayor continued, "so unless your man is some kind of Commie, I can't imagine your not going along with such a splendid scenario."

"He may be a lot of things, but he's no Commie, and I'd hate for the country to question his patriotism," Burt said. "So as long as I'm speaking for him, yes, he'll be there in his old red, white, and blues. And I couldn't be happier for the two of them when they light up the torch."

In my whole life, I had never witnessed such a rank betrayal. And to think he was my very best friend. So when I heard Jayne squeal at his words, I guess I did what any well-adjusted person does when they crack up. I fled.

I was sitting on the curb, where I could still hear the music and laughter from the *Trapeze* party. It was pouring rain, but I hardly noticed the water sluicing down the collar of my tux.

Then the rain stopped, but just on my head, since I could see it coming down in front of me, so I figured the martinis were still at work. Only it was an umbrella, and I looked up to see Burt holding it over me.

"Well, I got you out of it," he snapped—just the way he did at Clark Gable in *Run Silent, Run Deep* when he wouldn't give up the submarine.

"You mean it?" I said, hardly daring to believe my luck.

"Why I didn't leave you in that torch in the Statue of Liberty, I'll never know!"

I couldn't help thinking how in the end it's always your very best friend—the one you should know better than to trust in the first place —who comes through for you.

"How did you do it?" I said. I was so awestruck I sort of staggered getting to my feet, and if it hadn't been for those martinis, I'd have fallen for sure.

"I'll only tell you if you promise to take it like a man," Burt said. And he was even sterner now than he ever got with old Gable.

"I promise."

" I told them you were a fruit."

"Ohmigod!" I wailed.

"You promised!" And he raised the umbrella threateningly.

"I'm okay, I'm okay," I said real quick.

"I told them you were a fruit, *but*"—and he more than underlined that one particular word—"*but* patriotic, which was why you wanted to go through with the marriage. But you knew in your heart you couldn't, because you were a fruit."

I could already see *Confidential* and all the other supermarket scandal sheets devoting entire issues to the story. So there was no way I was about to blame Miss Hayworth if she did turn to the Fedeem brothers and marry all three of them, just to feel clean again.

It was impossible for Rita Hayworth to walk completely out of my life, unless I quit reading the newspapers altogether. Hardly a week went by where I didn't watch her schussing down an Alpine slope or sunning in Acapulco. I might have felt more encouraged about her future if the Fedeem brothers weren't invariably in the background.

Since I had last seen her, I had been made a partner in our company —now known as Hecht-Hill-Lancaster—and I had taken a fabulous apartment on Wilshire Boulevard in Westwood.

Even more impressive, I had this Japanese servant who could do just about everything. I'm not talking just about karate and sushi, but gourmet cuisine and origami napkin-folding. I had only to name it, and Mike could do it. That was what he told me to call him: Mike. It wasn't as Japanese as I would have liked, but then he didn't bow too well, either.

Ted discovered Mike. Ted was the secretary who became responsible for just about everything in my life. So when my driver's license was suspended for six months, Ted hired Mike to do the driving for me.

I was riding the crest of the wave but I wasn't enjoying it, and as the holiday party season approached I really crashed. Never having been a partygoer in the first place, I found myself with all this time on my hands. That was when I began fantasizing about holding an auction in which I'd put myself up for sale to the highest bidder. Naturally, the bidding would be limited to women, but what made the fantasy so nifty was it always ended the same way. I mean, I would be just about to get knocked down to some frustrated old harpy, with everything artificial about her except her money, when this soft voice, which made everything so still, would suddenly speak up. Then the hammer would fall, and I would be walking out with my new owner. Miss Rita Hayworth.

Somewhere along the line, I must have had one too many, because I confided the idea of the auction to Ted without mentioning Rita. Well, before I knew what was happening he had this big New Year's Eve party planned, with invitations sent out to a lot of people I'd heard of but never met.

It shows what a swell fellow Ted was, because he felt if there was one thing that might rouse me from my apathy, it would be to have a lot of women bidding for me.

Anyway, New Year's Eve rolled around, but no one showed up at the appointed hour. Since they were all prominent people, I was certain they had either read, or heard about my being a fruit. It was the kind of rejection I just couldn't take on a New Year's Eve, so I was about to administer my first double martini.

Only old Ted became very stern about that, because of the auction and not wanting the goods to stagger on the block. He went on to tell me that he had worked for the biggest people here and in Washington, D.C., and he had never seen anyone refuse an invitation to a party— no matter *what* they thought of the host.

It was as though everybody had waited outside so they could all be exactly one hour late, because suddenly my apartment was packed. I was looking around to see if the auctioneer had arrived, since I still hadn't figured how to handle that aspect of the evening, when I felt a hand on my arm.

I knew without turning whose it had to be. There was only one person who grabbed an arm and massaged it that way. Dorothy Dumont. She remained so startling in her off-beat beauty that I was at a loss for words.

"What's new?" I said. "The two most overworked words in the English language." She smiled at that, and she looked so evil doing it, I had to smile. "So what *is* new?"

"I've figured how to corner the gold market," she said.

"That's one secret I wouldn't want to share."

"I have no choice," she said. "I need an accomplice."

If anyone else made such casual banter, I'd laugh politely and get us both a drink. But the way she was looking at me, I knew I didn't want to fill that role, whether she was kidding or not.

"You've got Jack," I said. "He's tailor-made. He's not only your husband, but he loves you."

"I know, but I got bored one evening. I told him I was black."

It was like breathing for her, the way she said it so lightly, but it made me shudder underneath. I had never gotten over her marrying a black prizefighter who had fallen in love with her while she was passing as white.

"I'm surprised he didn't kill you," I said. Something I had expected to read in the newspapers every time I picked one up.

"It was on his mind." She got this satisfied, catlike smile. "At least, it was until he grabbed me by the throat, then it turned into the greatest night we ever had."

"You're still together, then?" I said hopefully.

"No. I left him. I knew we could never have another night like that one."

If there was one thing that intrigued me about Dorothy, it was her unabashed search for excitement. Any other woman with her animal attractiveness, along with her nimble mind, would have been content to let life come to her. But Dorothy made things happen. It was that touch of Satan in her.

"When I heard about the auction, I cashed in all my gilt-edged securities," she said confidentially. "I decided you were the perfect accomplice." Then she gave me that larcenous look of hers. "We're two of a kind; you can't deny it."

While the auction had been planned as no more than an excuse for the festivities, I had the feeling that Dorothy was joking on the level. I had the uneasy sense that my fantasy was about to come true. I had worried about some rich old harpy bidding for me, but never someone as hard to handle as Dorothy. I had to smile at myself for my cowardice, because Dorothy's brand of excitement was a rare commodity. If I'd had a little more of her larceny, I would have awaited the outcome with bated breath.

Instead, I planned to intercept the auctioneer and for a few extra bucks, I intended to have him knock me down to anyone *but* Dorothy. So I ducked out to the front gate where Mike was admitting the last of the guests and told him I would take over.

When I said my fantasy was becoming all too real, I hadn't begun to realize how real. If you'll remember, there was only one voice that could save me. I had turned away to light a cigarette against the wind when I heard it.

"Good evening."

I must have opened the gate, and I must have let her in, but I don't remember any part of that. All I remember was looking into those eyes. We might have still been standing there, if it had been up to me to break the spell.

"Are we in time for the auction?"

"Auction?" I said, trying to readjust my thinking. "What auction?"

"You told me there was going to be an auction," a male voice said.

"I did?"

"Yes, you did."

It took that long to realize I was talking to Bob Schiffer, who was standing there with his wife, Florence. They were old friends, who had obviously brought Rita with them. But all I could do was stare at her as though she might vanish if I turned away.

"We were afraid we might be late," Rita said. It was as if she felt she had to say something, what with me unable to take my eyes off her.

The one thing I didn't want was to go back inside. Not just because of Dorothy, which was reason enough, but now that I had the Princess with me, I had no intention of sharing her with a lot of strangers.

"The auction was just an excuse to get a lot of certain people to come over," I explained. "But if we go back in, then I won't be able to get back out."

This seemed to puzzle Rita. "Why would you have a party, if you want to escape from it?"

"I only invited the people I can't stand," I said. "Now that they're all inside, I can go anyplace I want and not have to worry about running into any of them."

She lit up my landscaped entryway with her smile. "I have never heard of such a wonderful reason for a party," she said.

That was all I needed to take her hand in mind, and the next thing, I had her moving with me and the Schiffers around the outside balcony, then on down the stairs to the street.

Everything I wanted in the world was now seated beside me in the back seat of the Schiffers' car, although she had managed to retrieve her hand. I couldn't have been less interested in where we were going, since I had a crucial point to clear up.

"I saw pictures of you in Acapulco and later on the ski slopes," I said to Rita, "but I could tell you had more on your mind than pleasure."

"You could?"

"I had the feeling you were traveling from place to place, speaking to writers and directors, in your search for a property to launch your company," I said. "There's nothing more grueling."

She gave me this little irritated sigh. "I got so tired of people telling me how lucky I was to spend my days doing nothing but skiing and sunning myself, when that was exactly what I was doing."

"I could tell."

"How?"

"I could tell by your drawn look, especially when you were skiing."

"You're the first person who saw that," she said, looking very pleased with me. "I've decided I'm no longer interested in developing properties to play in."

"You're not giving up acting?"

"No, I can't afford to," she said. "But I'm giving up the notion of having my own company."

There went the Fedeems, blown right out of the ballpark. It was going to be my night. I had taken a shot and POW! Bull's-eye.

"Happy New Year!" I suddenly shouted. It was a case of letting off steam or exploding.

I expected everyone to shout "Happy New Year" right back, which both Rita and Bob did, but not Florence. She was looking at me with a jaundiced eye. "It's your fault, Hill," she said, "that we are driving around in circles."

"Every time I think of a party to go to," Bob explained, "I think of someone I'll see there I can't stand."

"We could go down and look at Harold's boat," I said. I was being facetious, but I felt someone had to say something before Bob started circling the whole of Los Angeles.

In the very next turn of the steering wheel, Bob hit on the best possible solution for a New Year's Eve.

Here he was, just an ordinary man who made up faces—or anything else, if he forgot to put on his glasses—and he was suddenly inspired, which gives you an idea of what can happen when you're in a car with a Princess.

"We'll do better than that," Bob said. "We'll sail it."

Thinking back on that sail, it was like some kind of jeweled necklace where you remember each pearl, but not in their exact order, so rather than restring them, you let them sift sensuously through your fingers. Although I know that if I had been thinking, we would never have left the dock.

There was a monumental difference between talking about a 100-foot boat and boarding it with the intent of taking it to sea. That yacht suddenly seemed as big as an ocean liner. In my secret thoughts, I wondered how it was even possible to manage her with a crew of eight, which was her regular complement, not counting the captain.

So when I sensed a certain hesitation on the part of the others, I would cheerfully have settled for a few drinks and some Happy New Year's dockside, if Rita hadn't turned those eyes of hers on me.

"What do you think?" she said.

"I don't want to influence anyone," I said boldly, "and I haven't even had a drink yet. But I had something of a reputation as a sailor on Lake Washington."

"Lake Washington . . . ?" Rita said.

"In Seattle. They've probably turned out more Olympic winners than any other sailing region in the country," I said. "I went to college up there."

"In that case," Rita quickly spoke up, which told me how anxious she was for us to take the boat out, "I know we can manage."

* * *

Rita had disappeared with Flossy in search of more practical clothes, so Bob and I were taking advantage of the moment to have a tot of rum, as all good seafaring men do before shoving off.

I had started calling him "Captain" Schiffer after the first couple of sips, which could have been my first mistake. I hadn't done it to flatter him, but like I told him, there's something reassuring to women at sea to know there's a captain aboard.

It wasn't more than a couple of sips later when Schiffer said, in his newfound captain's voice, "I'd like to know more about how you won your reputation as a sailor on Lake Washington."

It was something I hadn't planned on getting into, so I shrugged modestly. "It was nothing."

"I'd like to know more, Hill."

It was the first time he had ever called me by my last name, and in this real stern voice. I was so startled I even began telling him the actual story of that long-ago day in naval history when I was taking this sailing lesson on Lake Washington from a fraternity brother who owned a dinghy. It was the day of the annual regatta when Washington rowed against California.

I had just made the wrong move in a gust of wind, which cost us our sail. We started to sink, causing an embarrassing number of beer bottles to surface around us. And worst of all, we held up the whole race while the coast guard rescued us.

So if I had told that whole story, it's a cinch we would never have left the dock, which might well have put the kibosh on my new relationship with Rita. But luckily, I caught myself. I told Captain Schiffer it was such a lengthy story I'd have to finish it another time. He gave me a funny look, but I was into my second tot, which I quickly downed. Then we went topside and got underway.

I don't remember us working really well together, until I began saluting him after we stole below for another tot. I could tell he liked it, even though he told me not to do it too openly, especially when his wife was looking. I understood that, because I'd heard that in any happy marriage it's the wife who gets the saluting.

As we motored through San Pedro Harbor on our way out to sea, and Rita came on deck, everything took on a whole new meaning.

She was bundled up against the cold and the night. All you could see were those fabulous eyes looking over the high collar of a pea jacket, which Captain Schiffer's wife must have found for her.

With her standing behind the Captain at the helm, I could tell his confidence was growing with every salute, because he was ordering me all over the place. I also understood for the first time why they drank all that rum when they sank the Spanish Armada. I mean, when you're shorthanded, each 140-proof tot seems to double the size of your crew, something the Captain confided to me after we had the last one. So for strategic reasons we decided we'd have a tot every hour on the hour, until in the Captain's eyes, we had taken on the normal complement of eight hands.

If you've ever been in San Pedro Harbor on New Year's Eve aboard a 100-foot racing sloop with a mast that seemed about twice that high, then you know about those mean-spirited fellows who sit in their little glass towers controlling the bridges. They're supposed to snap to it when you honk your horn—because if they don't open up, and you don't slow down, POW! There goes your mast.

At the first one, Captain Schiffer had to come to a dead standstill while the fellow in the tower roused himself to open up, which showed what kind of a New Year's Eve *he* was celebrating. But by the time we got to the next one, we had dropped another tot, and old Schiff only slowed a little. I almost stopped breathing, but the bastard got it up without making us wait.

When we got to the last bridge, it was really something, because Captain Schiffer made it clear he wasn't slowing down for anything, and the bastard in the tower waited him out. Then, at the last split second, he opened her up, and I swear there wasn't more than an inch between our mast and that rising span.

As much as I was enjoying the drama, I was seeing a brand-new side of Rita, she was that excited. I don't know why it should have come as such a surprise, but it was clear to me that the only thing that could have made it better for her would have been for us to sweep away the whole bridge and that petty tyrant in the tower with it. Even if the mast had come crashing down in the process, I guarantee she wouldn't have flinched. It was unguarded moments like these that gave me the only clues to what was going on inside her. It simply wasn't in her makeup to reveal her emotions, or what was bothering her, or anything else.

So when I knew in that moment that the search for excitement was as important in her life as it was in mine, it was a revelation of sheer beauty. I had wanted to hug her before, but not the way I wanted to right then. So I settled for my first salute to her. Her mouth was hidden by the collar of that pea jacket, but I knew I had made her smile. I could see it in her eyes.

I hardly had time to savor the first intimate moment between us, when Captain Schiffer, who was getting more and more like Bligh, reveling in his newfound power, ordered me to ready this tremendous sail since we had moved out to sea.

There was enough canvas to cover the Ringling Brothers Barnum & Bailey Circus. It was getting very rough now we had left the harbor. Once I moved to attach that enormous tent to the boom, it was all I could do to keep my feet.

A great gust of wind caught me completely unaware. It lifted up the sail with me clinging to it, and I thought for sure I was about to be dropped right into the ocean. Suddenly, there it was, right below me. But a mighty wave brought the boat around, and the next thing I knew I was back on deck, with the vast sail settled down over me. That was when I knew what it was like to be in darkest Africa.

Luckily, I had my handy pencil flashlight, which I had been carrying for about eight years so I could read theater programs. It was like Stanley bumping into Livingston, only I don't think they were under a tent, and I know for sure, neither of them was ever mistaken for a love goddess.

"Are you all right?" I asked, since I knew how roughly that wave must have flung her about. After all, she had been behind the wheel when last I saw her, and now I had no idea where we were, other than still on the deck.

"Yes," she said, in her real soft way. "Are you?"

"I am now," I said, and I found myself lowering my voice, which always happened once she spoke. "I guess we're lucky to still be aboard. And it's the first moment we've had alone. That's why I figure we're really lucky."

"I've got nothing against being alone," she said, "but if we decide to do it again, there must be an easier way, don't you think?"

The tiny pencil light beam searched for her in the darkness.

"I've been dying to ask what made you come tonight?"

"The auction," she said.

I couldn't blame myself for smiling a little triumphantly at that. "Were you going to bid on me?"

She studied me with those great sad eyes of hers. "I felt I had to tell you something first, before you did anything so desperate."

"I guess it was kind of desperate," I admitted. "Putting myself up for auction like that."

"You could have fallen into the wrong hands."

I had never planned on really holding the auction, but that was what she could do—the way she was so intent with her eyes and her listening. I mean she had me suddenly believing everything I said.

"I just didn't care," I said. Even though I warned myself, it was hard to keep from laying it on. Especially since I had never dreamed of such a romantic opportunity, what with the tent over us and the absolute darkness and the intimacy. "But I care now. I can't begin to tell you how much I care. I can hardly wait to hear what you have to tell me."

She dropped those long, slender fingers on my hand holding the pencil flashlight. "I was wrong about your sharpening the saws," she said. "I don't know what made me think that."

I can't tell you why she felt it was so vital for me to know that before the auction. But it brought out the dimestore analyst in me.

"It was your subconscious speaking—that hidden voice that directs all of our lives," I said. I couldn't keep the Freudian resonance from my voice, I was that sure of my ground. So you can imagine my surprise when Rita not only took her fingers back, but got this wary look.

"You really *believe* that sort of thing?" she said.

"Yes, I do. It could have been your subconscious, wishing I had always been part of your life—even way back when you were doing the magic act," I said. "I wouldn't be surprised if I wound up helping you around your house, especially when help was hard to find, say at Christmastime. In that part of your subconscious mind, I mean, where I scrubbed your floors, and stole caviar, and did all those helpful sort of things."

I could see the old wariness fading, and in its place an excitement, and all those flecks of color glinting in her eyes.

"If you did all that for me," she said, "even if it was only in my subconscious, then I would have been a fool *not* to have put in a bid for you at auction."

"How high do you think you might have gone?" I said. "I wouldn't want you to have risked too much."

"I know, I don't have to think," she said. I had never heard her so positive. "One hundred forty thousand dollars and fifty cents."

I gasped. Not even Dorothy Dumont had that kind of money!

Suddenly, the tent was thrown back, and there was Captain Bligh. But not really. He couldn't have looked more worried, until he saw that we were both alive. Then right away he called for a ration of rum, and that was when the real Bligh stepped forward in the person of his good wife.

It was like this Pulitzer Prize novelist once told me, when we had taken a moment from the toils of scriptwriting to have a breather at the hotel bar. He said that to be successful every man had to have an anchor. I really didn't know what he meant at the time, and before I could pursue it, he slipped off the stool and passed out. So it wasn't until later when I ran into Nunnally Johnson, who really got me started in this business—which was why he felt he owed me something—that I understood the anchor thing. Nunnally told me that behind every successful man there was a woman holding him back.

That was why I couldn't have felt better for Bob—what with that canvas sail flapping all over the place, and no one at the wheel, and nothing in his future, or in him, but rum—than I did to discover he had his anchor. As you can see, he was just about to go off the deep end when his loved one not only held him back, but shut down the bar as well.

Although when we dropped the ship's anchor in a cove at Catalina, I managed to get a bottle of champagne before Captain Bligh's helpmate declared the bar off limits. Then I slipped into the cabin where

I had told Rita we might enjoy another moment alone, since I had one further pressing question for her.

It had gotten colder than I thought, and Rita sat wrapped up to the chin in blankets on top of a bunk. I could hardly believe it, when she told me she still had the pea jacket on underneath all that. It was like finding yourself in the Arctic with an Eskimo. No wonder they never got beyond rubbing noses. It explained why they were dying out as a race.

Be all that as it may, I was still anxious to find out what had made her decide on the figure of one hundred forty thousand dollars and fifty cents.

She said that when she was in Ireland, she had gone horseback riding by herself. She was following a wooded stream when she ran into a caravan of tinkers. There was a card game going on among the men, who were playing for the most beautiful home she had ever seen. It was on wheels, all hand carved and drawn by four magnificent horses.

She said the man who won it was big and dark and swarthy, and somehow she knew he cheated, even though no one called him on it. She asked if he would be willing to sell the house. He quoted her a price of one hundred forty thousand dollars and fifty cents.

Since she didn't have that much money, she said she had forgotten about it until after she saw me again. Then she began to have a recurring dream, in which I made it possible for her to get her very first home.

"Were you married in the dream?" I had to ask that, because I already had been stuck once with the Prince, when I was a French tour guide, and then with Orson and those lousy saws when I was a magician's assistant.

Rita grew thoughtful. "No, now that I think of it, I wasn't."

That made me feel better. "But fifty cents," I said. "That's what gets me. One hundred forty thousand dollars and fifty cents." I had been working on this cork all the time she had been talking. Now it exploded from the bottle, and champagne came gushing out, splashing onto the cabin floor.

"That was what was so wonderful about the dream," Rita went on, as if people fired off Dom Perignon whenever she talked about her dreams. "You had such talent for cards, you only had to ante fifty cents to get into the first pot. So in the end, after you had won the house from the big, dark, swarthy tinker, who I just knew was a cheater, that was all the money you had risked. But you were really worth the other one hundred forty thousand. Now maybe you can see why I didn't have to be married—I had you."

If ever I was shocked with myself at having doubted my talents, it had to be right then. I had gone and gotten the figures all backwards. So once I realized that, I also realized that here was the most glamorous star in the picture business, and all she wanted was a house, her own house, and don't think I wasn't going to get it for her, even if it cost more than fifty cents.

In spite of all those blankets around her, all I could think of was making a stab at a hug, as soon as I mopped up the champagne I was wading in. So I grabbed a curtain off a porthole, got down on my hands and knees, and started mopping, when she suddenly gave an excited cry.

"*Now* I remember you!" she said. "You're the one who scrubbed my floors!"

"And waxed them, too!" I added proudly.

"And gave me caviar, and the Christmas tree!" She was incandescent at her discovery. "Of *course* I remember you!"

It had been a long and trying period, but suddenly everything seemed so right with the world that I wasn't even aware of her glasses. She had to be a relative of Houdini, the way she had managed to produce them out from under those blankets and that pea jacket. And there she was, putting them on and peering at me like a teacher with a new pupil. Her eyes kept getting bigger, and all the wonderful radiance left her magnificent face.

"You know," she said, "you have a *rotten* reputation."

I had been anxious for her to recognize me, but now she had, I hadn't expected her to look so deep inside. I just stood there at a loss.

"You really do, you know," she said. Then she sighed, the most soul-wrenching sigh I had ever heard. It was as though she recognized that after all the husbands, and now me, it was just too much. I watched that great mane of auburn hair nod slowly forward, until her chin rested on her chest. I had to bend forward to hear her next words, they were so faint.

"You have the rottenest reputation I have ever met."

She had fallen asleep. It had all been too much for her. I hung the curtain full of Dom Perignon back over the porthole, so she would know when she woke up that I was really a fine housekeeper, on the long odds she still wanted me to get her that house. Then I took a last look at her, and she looked so helpless all bundled up like that, and so alone, I could have cried.

Even though it was probably too late, I made up my mind to start cleaning up my way of life just in case. So the first thing I did when I got up on deck was to throw away the pencil flashlight.

When I'd said I carried it all the time to read theater programs, I lied. John Swift, who looked and acted like a deacon but who really wrote westerns, was the one who gave it to me. He was also the one who dropped forks, then probed around under restaurant tables with a pencil flashlight, making passes. So what I did on that windy deck was to make up my mind never to lie to Rita Hayworth. No matter what! At least she could always remember me as the person who had a really rotten reputation but never lied.

I can't tell you how much better I began to feel. So when Schiffer came up, we put our heads together, since it was obvious his position with the old anchor wasn't much better than mine. We needed a diversion. There was hardly anything pertaining to the sea old Schif didn't know. Like how to steal lobsters out of those lobster pots. So he put up one little sail called a jib so that we could silently steal across the water like those Arabs. And by the time the sun was high in the sky, we were anchored in another cove and the smell of lobsters grilling brought the two ladies up on deck.

Right away, Schif's anchor wanted to know where we got the lobsters, because lobster poaching was a terrible thing to do, I guess, what with there being a big fine, and a jail sentence, and everything. Since I had made my vow never to lie in Rita Hayworth's presence, I told her that we had stolen them.

Well, I never ate so many grilled lobsters in my life, because the ladies vanished right back below. I'll never forget the reproachful look Rita gave me. That was the way the day ended, too. Real subdued. When the Schiffers dropped Rita and me off at my apartment so that I could drive her back to her place, there wasn't much more to say to them other than that it had been swell, and good sailing, and a Happy New Year, of course.

Like I told you, they had taken my driver's license away, but I was afraid if I brought that up as an excuse to keep her around, she would simply call a cab. She looked so sad and fragile, still wearing that oversized pea jacket with the collar up, as though she might never get warm again.

I just knew if I didn't leave her in a happier mood, I would never be able to sleep again, since I couldn't help but feel I was responsible.

"Shall we have one for the road?"

She didn't even bother to answer, which made me realize what a dumb question for someone with my reputation to have asked. So I quickly said I wanted to get her advice about a close mutual friend. I told her it would be a chance to really warm up, too. Then I could take her home.

At least that got her upstairs to my apartment, although she still hadn't said a word. And even when I asked if I could take her coat, she just shook her head.

Anyway, I don't know what got me onto Schif, except he was the only close mutual friend we had. I told her how I had always gone out of my way on the set to get to know the little people, since I had once been a junior writer and had experienced what it was like to have a big producer walk onto a set and ignore me.

I didn't come right out and say I was the same as that big producer today, and Schif, with his powder puffs, was like me in my days as a lowly junior writer with my pencils. I didn't want to lay it on too heavy now that I'd quit lying.

So I went on to tell her that if I hadn't been all that democratic—and not just to makeup men, but other minorities as well—I would never have gotten to know the other side of Schif. I mean the side that knew *her*, which I liked to think of as the creative side.

Well, she sat down at that, but I have to admit it was probably due to the weight of that pea jacket. So I went on to tell her that Schif had accomplished something that neither Harold nor Burt—not even

Arthur Krim and United Artists—had accomplished which was to produce her into my life to make this an unforgettable New Year.

"Many a champion walks the street unknown," I concluded.

It was one of my favorite lines—one that great writer Vincent Lawrence once used after his play failed and we had been drunk for about a week (he was referring to a bartender we had come to like). I let her believe the line was mine, because it wasn't important right then who said it, or why, although for the first time she really looked at me.

I lost it once and for all, as I watched those eyes of hers fill with tears. It was like that first time at her house, when she gave old Harry's kid the present and looked right through her into the far distance.

If ever I had wanted to come to her rescue but instead had helplessly to watch her get up, then follow her out the door and down the stairs, it was then. I couldn't stop talking.

"I know I've already mentioned it, but I can't get over how Schif outproduced all those big names. I mean, I'm talking about a real producer. Anyway, that's what I wanted your advice about, since you know that other side of him. I mean, he may be another Irving Thalberg." I saw her into her side of the car and closed the door. "Many a champion walks the street unknown."

I repeated that last line on my way around the back of the car to my side, and that did it. I didn't have another thing to say. And it was a cinch she wasn't about to say anything. It never even entered my mind that I had no driver's license. Or that if I got stopped, it meant an automatic six-month jail sentence. I couldn't have cared less.

It wasn't until we pulled up in front of her house and I felt I would never see her again that I had to make one last try. "I wanted to ask you in Paris, and I wanted to ask you in New York, and I wanted to ask you yesterday on New Year's Eve," I said. "I've been dying to know about your painting."

I didn't know what to expect, but she turned to me and she finally saw me. "Why *didn't* you?"

I had no idea I had been that tense, because I started to smile, even though I didn't know why. "I guess I was too ashamed," I said. "I did all that talk about writing, and I haven't written a word."

"You said that was how we would spend the years—you writing, me painting."

"That's what I said, all right." I had to shake my head, I was that impressed, the way she hadn't forgotten one word.

She was really looking at me now, and all those wonderful lights and flecks of color were back in her eyes. She was almost smiling.

"You said we'd please ourselves, and that was all we'd worry about pleasing."

It was crazy how once I got looking into her eyes, I was hardly aware of what I was saying. As if I was talking in my sleep . . .

"I almost came back that night," I said.

"Maybe you should have," she said, very softly.

"I really liked you that Christmas Eve," I said. "Did you like me?"

Talk about talking in your sleep! You can see how unwary I'd gotten, asking a question like that. I mean, it was really risking a rejection slip—and after all my careful training in the oblique approach.

"I know I liked what you had to say," she said. "I don't think there's been a day I haven't thought about your words."

"Then you knew who I really was the time I came to your hotel in Paris with Burt and his wife?" She kind of frowned and studied me, like she was thinking on that. "And you made that up, about my being a guide, and sharpening saws and all?"

"Did I say that?"

"And when you pretended to realize who I was, after I started mopping up the champagne on the boat. . . ? You were really just pretending?"

I knew I was making her smile, and I can't tell you how much I loved doing it. She sort of shook her head. "I'm not that skillful an actress."

If she could fool me like she had, she had to be another Sarah Bernhardt. Only she'd be the last to know it, which was why I just sat and looked at her. And what made it really nifty was she just sat and looked at me.

You can understand me tossing away a day or two just looking at

her. Only for her to be happy just looking at me meant the beginning
of her seeing beyond my reputation and into my heart. I don't mean
to brag, but I really have to care about someone to let them do that.

Anyway, the streetlights went on, and I don't know why, but it
gave me an extra-warm feeling, like when she discovered I had hung
her painting on that Christmas Eve.

"Are you going to show me what you've painted?" I said.

She was suddenly serious. I can't tell you how serious. "I haven't
lifted a brush," she said.

Then she started to laugh, and then we were both laughing. Really
laughing, I mean.

Only, almost as suddenly as she had started laughing, she stopped.
"What is it?" I said, and that sense of panic returned, because I was
sure it was something that would take her inside her house.

"We've got to go back to your place," she said. "We forgot something."

It was like the warden unstrapping you from the chair. You don't
ask questions, you just get moving. If ever I risked a ticket and a six-
month jail sentence, I did it getting her back to my digs.

"Can I help?" I said, once we were in the apartment.

"Yes, I think you can," she said. "We forgot to have one for the
road."

You'll remember that I was the one who had asked a certain head
of United Artists if he thought she had a sense of humor. And he was
the one who had replied, why should she bother, when she already
had the world at her feet. I just had to gloat a little over that one,
because I really liked Arthur, and never more than right then. And
everybody else, too, who had lent a hand, like Schif and his anchor.

Now that I had all this newfound courage I had one more bridge
to cross.

"I know you're probably going to laugh, but I have to say it, since
it's been on my mind constantly—even more than your painting.
And I don't even know whether people do it anymore. Hug, I mean.
I just want to hug you."

For a moment, I almost wished she had laughed, she got that
serious, and I thought she was going to cry. Then she sort of smiled
with her eyes.

"Maybe you'd better take my coat," she said.

It sure wasn't ermine, or mink, like I had sworn it would have to be. But that pea coat was the single most beautiful coat I had ever hung up.

"I can't get over," I called to her, "how lucky it was, the Schiffers dropping you off, instead of taking you home."

Then in that soft, soft voice, that made everything so very still, she called back. "I asked them to."

PART THREE

PART THREE

'VE always been fascinated by the way anthropologists seem compelled to give convenient labels to the ages of man—Pleistocene, Miocene, Holocene, and so forth. It was Rita who came up with the label for the next period in our lives—she called it "the days of the cave."

Since she was the inspiration, the first step in establishing this new order was the cave-holder's stocking up on Dom Perignon. It's crucial to keep the personality of the person with whom you're sharing the cave uppermost in your mind. You order not one bottle of Dom Perignon, but a month's supply. And, of course, the caviar. Figure a month's supply there, too. It wasn't that we weren't coming out for a month, but it was the psychological edge we'd possess just knowing we had the option.

A true cave, we found, was like a fortress. It had to be sealed off. That meant locking the outside iron gate, along with every other entrance. No one is to be trusted, except the person with whom you're sharing the premises. Then the phones must be concealed in drawers and places where they can barely be heard. It is, however, very important still to be *able* to hear them, because it tells you the outside world continues to want you, but you don't want them.

Once you've done all that, it's a question of ambiance. Turn the air conditioning all the way down, especially if it's kind of warm out, which should make it next to freezing. That means you've got to keep a roaring fire going in all the fireplaces. This requires staying close together, which in turn guarantees hugging.

If you've given up lying, as I had, there is some danger of running out of conversation. But the fire obviates that. It's hypnotic when you get to staring into those flames. But with Rita, I found that the only staring I did was into those eyes of hers. So I guess all the fires could have gone out and we'd still have stayed warm, which says it all for hugging.

If I forgot to mention it, keep the champagne iced. Preferably in a bucket on rollers, so it's right next to whichever fire you're next to. Keep the caviar in that same container. And the music! A great stereo is *de rigueur*.

Everyone has their own guidelines on what the ideal cavewoman should wear. In my case, I favored the youthful look for Rita. She had her hair pulled back with one of those barettes. She was wearing a blouse and skirt and neck scarf, which made her appear no more than sixteen. She'd never looked more beautiful.

"Here's to us," I said, raising my glass.

"Here's to us," she said, "and the days of the cave."

I was poking at the fire, but I was watching her out of the corner of my eye. When she saw me studying her, she shook her head.

"It doesn't seem possible."

"What doesn't?" I said.

"We're finally doing something about it."

"It's been a long time."

"That Christmas Eve—that really was the beginning, wasn't it?"

"It certainly was."

"What would you have bet," she said, then paused. "What odds would you have given that we'd never do anything about it?"

I didn't have to think, but I pretended to. "After the Prince walked in," I said, "about a million to one."

She gazed into the fire for a moment before she spoke. "When I did see you again, it didn't hit me at first that you were you."

"You mean the afternoon I came for tea with Burt and his wife?"

She nodded. "Was that your idea?" she said. "Bringing Norma?"

"No, it wasn't mine."

"She made you both seem so very respectable. She seemed so perfect for the role of producer's wife with her lovely looks and manners, I thought at first you must have gotten her out of the Paris office of Central Casting."

"I kept figuring you'd remember me if I could just get you to put on your glasses," I said.

She glanced up at me. "That's what I've been thinking about. The look on your face when I took you for a guide."

"I spent most of that night trying to figure how to set you straight."

"I didn't know what to expect," she said. "So it was quite a surprise when I saw you the next morning in the lobby. And with caviar!"

"For me the diciest moment was the night of the *Trapeze* party. I thought I'd lost you for sure when Burt made his announcement about Jayne and me."

That glint came into her eyes—the one I'd seen on rare occasions before. If I was right about it, it means that she was beginning to laugh inside. But she was such a good actress, and I was never all that sure.

"That was a shocker, all right," she said, nodding, "to no more than finish our first dance only to discover you were about to get married."

"What do you think it was to me?" I said. "It was the first I'd heard of it, too."

That seemed to surprise her. "It was?"

"We got our signals crossed, Burt and me. He was meant to be dancing with *you* when he said all those things he did to Jayne."

"Oh."

"I tried to find you. I wanted to explain everything, but all I could find was the orchid," I said.

"I left it in case you changed your mind," she said.

I was amazed. Especially at the matter-of-fact way she said it. "You mean you left it on purpose?" I said. "I'd have sworn you'd flung it away in disgust."

"No, just the opposite," she said. "I figured if I left it by the door, the first person you'd question would be the doorman. So I left a message with him, telling you where to find me." And that was when she smiled. Not a big one, but enough to let me know what was going on inside. "Now that that's behind us, we have no more excuses," she said.

I didn't know what she meant, but I was enjoying myself too much to care. "We haven't?"

"No. So I'd better get out the paints, and you'd better sharpen some pencils."

It was like that first time I had seen her in Tijuana. And even though she was smiling at the moment, she never seemed completely to lose that vulnerable look she had then, the one that reminded me of a fawn fleeing a fire.

So in the next breath, I told her about that trip with my family. And how I had decided to make a deal for her, only her father had come along. That got her smiling even more. I've never found anything that could get me smiling like her smile—up to and including old W. C. Fields movies.

"Imagine," I said, "I couldn't have had more than twenty-five dollars that I had saved from my paper route, but I figured I could buy you for that."

"It was a lot of money at that age."

"I thought so."

"So you were really very wise."

"I was?"

"You saved your money—and now you have me."

I had her, but briefly, because at that moment a cloud of smoke billowed out of the kitchen. Too late, I remembered I had put a skillet on the stove with oil to pop corn.

I was about to close the front door, which I had thrown open to clear the smoke out, when I saw Mrs. Bedlington at the outer iron gate. I immediately closed the door behind me, so Rita couldn't over hear us.

Mrs. Bedlington owned the apartment. Her full name was Mrs. Schuyler Tunstill Bedlington the Fourth. To be risking laughs with a moniker like that, a person has to be really loaded.

When I first started looking for a place, Ted had warned me there was no chance to get this one, because the owner wouldn't rent to people in the entertainment community. But he suggested I take a look anyway just to give him a better idea of what I had in mind.

Although she lived in Bel-Air, Mrs. Bedlington made a point of screening all her tenants, so Ted arranged a meeting. I've never seen so many jewels on a single person. She could hardly walk, she was so tightly laced into some kind of armor under her dress. She was such an obvious snob, I couldn't help piling on the flattery—complimenting her on her diamonds, her voice. And once I got started, it was hard to stop. Before I was through, I'd set visions dancing in her blue-rinsed head of singing in an operetta our company was planning called *The Lady from Brazil*. I don't know what made me come up with such a corny title. I guess that was why I invoked our company, to give it a ring of authenticity. That was when she told me she had never leased to anyone in the picture business, but she had decided to make a single exception.

Since I was unmarried, she said, she took it for granted that I would be the sole occupant. She said she had no patience with so-called "modern ways" or Hollywood scandal. She suggested we embark on a month-to-month arrangement; if at any point either of us was unhappy with the other, we could call it off.

If she had been an ordinary snob, I would have walked away. But I've always admired the best—and she was the most professional snob I had ever met. It was also the most fabulous apartment I had ever seen.

In my wildest dreams, I'd never imagined Rita and me together in that apartment. I mean even a *visit* by Rita would have set the owner on edge. The only other time I'd had anyone over had been the New Year's party, and Ted had made sure Mrs. Bedlington the Fourth was out of town before he began the party preparations.

Now there she was at the iron gate, rambling on about her trip to Paris, and how her first thought on getting back had been of me and of what progress we were making on *The Lady from Brazil*.

It goes to show, if you want to keep your cave intact, don't have any truck with the outside world. Because if it wasn't a Mrs. Bedlington, it would be something equally unfortunate.

My first reaction was to tell Rita everything. But once I stepped back inside our sanctuary I decided to put off any mention of Mrs. Bedlington until later. We had shut out the world. That was all that was important to Rita. I intended to keep it that way. Of all the things I can remember, they were the very best, those days in our cave.

* * *

Like all knowledgeable cave dwellers of old, we waited for the curtain of night to fall that first time we ventured out. As we locked the iron gate behind us, I explained to Rita that the only animals who had survived from the beginning of the universe were nocturnal.

We went to Dominick's. He was an old crony from my New York days. I had been a fifteen-dollar-a-week page boy when I met him. He had run the bar in this small but nifty Times Square hotel. At least it seemed nifty, because Dom was always good for a drink, or a meal, or even a loan if you were out of cash, which most of us perpetually were.

Now he had a little restaurant which he ran from behind the bar, while his wife, Peggy, took care of the kitchen. I don't know which of them deserved the most credit for its success, because I never ate one of her meals without a few of his martinis first. Since he made the world's greatest martini, I thought she was the world's greatest cook.

We were in a booth finishing our dinner, when Rita paused to look at me. "You know, I'm glad we came," she said. "I'm glad, because I had begun to feel that I would never bring myself to the point where I'd go out again."

"Maybe we should do this more often," I said. "Like twice a month."

She didn't smile, because she didn't hear me. She had gone walkabout again into her memories.

"It reminds me of high school," she said, so at least I knew where she was. "I loved high school, but I dreaded graduation. I knew once it came I couldn't go back—that I'd be dancing full time." Then, because she had revealed something about herself, she immediately attempted to dismiss it. "I know it's not the same."

She wrapped up her whole youth in that wistful statement.

Once we left Dominick's, I decided things were going too well to press my luck, so I didn't risk using the elevator when we got back to the apartment. Instead, I showed Rita five other ways of getting up to my place without being seen. She was really impressed. I told her she wouldn't have to worry about running into strangers, or someone wanting an autograph.

"I'd have the opening pages of my manuscript in one hand, flowers in the other. . . ." Rita Hayworth and James Hill after their wedding.

Courtesy of the Billy Rose Theater Collection, The New York Public Library

"In spite of old baggy work jeans, even in spite of having no makeup on . . . she had these wide-set eyes like no one I had ever seen."

Globe Photos

"He [Harry Cohn] had a terrible reputation for being a tyrant. . . ."

" 'It was Orson [Welles] she was with when she first met you. . . . She remembered how you kept the saws sharp for his magic act. . . .' "

The Lester Glassner Collection

"We wound up at a gambling casino. It featured a couple known as the Dancing Cansinos."

"It's amazing how many successful people grow up without ever having had a youth. . . ."

"If I talked enough about me and my family, it was just a matter of living into the next century . . . until I knew everything there was to know about her and her family."

"She had that sad, faraway look in her eyes again."

"I figured after all these years of playing parts you hated—parts that capitalized on an image you loathed—you would do anything, suffer anything to change."

Bob Landry, Life Magazine, © Time Inc.

The Lester Glassner Collection

"I'd grown so used to seeing her and the Prince [Aly Khan] surrounded by
an entourage, and invariably at some international race meet."

"Everything depended on her directing that gaze of hers at me.
Now she had her glasses on, that is."

" 'If I could have done the part [in *Separate Tables*] in the theater as well as
your wife did it on the screen,' Margaret Leighton told me, 'they'd never
have had her take my place.' "

"In the history of the movie business, there have only been one or two beautiful women who had a true comedic talent. . . ."

" 'I thought it might put me back to sleep,' she said, 'and I almost made it with *They Came to Cordura.*' "

"Everything began to come apart for me in Durango. . . . I could begin to see a change in Rita."

"She'd said she would do *Cordura* so we could get the house . . . then she had agreed to do one more picture . . . the comedy, for me."

"I realized it wasn't the presence of the media, but what I might tell them about the bandage, that was worrying her."

"Those two old codgers caddying for us were cap-over-golf-bags in love with her . . . because of the lovely rhythm of her swing."

"Marriage to Rita made my mode of travel something I previously associated only with royalty."

Hill: "Have you ever thought of taking the global view?" Hayworth: "No, but I think I'd like to." Rita Hayworth with Willy Brandt.

It wasn't until we were back in the cave, settled in front of a fire, that she asked me, "Why did you feel you needed all those different ways of slipping up here without being seen? I can understand a married man having all those escape routes. Especially if he had a mistress in the same building. But you're not married."

While she was making a joke of it, I could see she was dead serious underneath. I knew in that instant that I would never give her any cause for suspicion. Not now or in the future.

"No, but I'm contemplating it," I said. I looked at her hard, so there could be no doubt in her mind of who I had in my mind. "Only when I do, I don't want a place with escape routes. I want a carved wooden house with a vegetable garden."

Our days fell into a pattern in which I began to get the feeling of respectability that I had always associated with bankers and all those other tie-wearing, briefcase-toting citizens who kissed their bride at the door before racing off to work in the morning.

All that changed when Rita started shooting *Pal Joey*, a musical they were making with her and Frank Sinatra at Columbia. So we started dropping her off. I say we, because Mike still did the driving since my license continued suspended. Mike was doing a lot more bowing these days, and without my ever suggesting it. I guess even in Tokyo it means a little something extra to start the day off with a princess in the car.

Rita's day began at 5:30 in the A.M. I knew Burt was a fanatic when it came to getting in shape for a movie, but she was every bit as self-disciplined and demanding. It would be 6:30 that same night, eleven hours later, when Mike would collect me before picking her up. She would still be in her makeup. I never ceased to marvel at how she could get into the car, and—no matter how tired she was—regale me with marvelously comic anecdotes about what went on on the set.

Naturally, at my place of business, my partners were amazed at my newfound industry. I was the first to arrive and the last to leave. I worried about that at first, because if anything, it's got to make your partners jumpy. I would have told Burt and Harold about Rita, but once they knew I had someone turning the keys in the fortress, they'd have figured I was in the same situation they were in—just one more member of the old ball-and-chain brigade.

All of which brings me to one particular night, which was like no other night because it signaled the first break in our solidarity. Rita was leaving the following morning for San Francisco, where Columbia had scheduled a week of location shooting on *Pal Joey*.

Once we arrived at the garage in the basement of the apartment building, Rita went on up ahead, while Mike and I gathered up the shopping he had done along with a number of extras she intended to take on her trip. We had no sooner stepped onto the balcony that circled the top floor, when who should materialize but Mrs. Schuyler Tunstill Bedlington Four.

"Well!" she said in this real cold, angry voice.

I could tell by the pinched look on her face that the armor under her dress had been tightened up a notch. I didn't figure on Mike showing such a cowardly streak. Not that I expected a karate chop, but he grabbed the packages from me and made a beeline down the balcony and in through my iron gates.

"Well!" she exploded, looking after him.

"Man oh man, Mrs. Schuyler Tunstill Bedlington the Fourth, you really make a person's day," I said, chuckling. "You truly do."

She turned from looking after Mike. "Well!"

"That sums it all up, so don't say another word. You're as rare as a ruby, Mrs. Bedlington, you're one of a kind," I said, and started past her.

"Miss Hayworth just entered your apartment!" She underlined and measured each one of those words.

I paused and frowned. "I beg your pardon."

"I just saw Miss Rita Hayworth enter your apartment."

My frown deepened—I was pretending to be that puzzled. "You let her in?"

"She had her own key."

I started chuckling all over again, only it was my real relieved chuckle. "Oh . . ." I said, nodding, ". . . my maid."

She really strained the old armor the way she stiffened. "Your *maid*?"

"I'd appreciate it if you didn't mention the resemblance," I said, lowering my voice. "It's tough enough to get any real work out of them, and I was hoping she'd do my windows."

"Well . . ."

She said it a lot more softly this time. "Like I said, Mrs. Bedlington, that says it all."

"You promised not to have any live-in help, when we agreed upon the lease," she said. "She *is* living in, isn't she?"

"Mrs. Bedlington, let me level with you," I said as I eased her away from the balcony into a secluded corner. And with my arm around her shoulders, I lowered my voice almost to a whisper. "That girl is my niece from Ireland on my mother's side."

I explained how my niece's mother hoped that by being sent to me she would learn a worthwhile trade and forget about everyone telling her she looked like a movie star. I also warned Mrs. Bedlington against mentioning anything about her uncanny resemblance to Rita Hayworth, in case she saw her doing my windows. "I don't even want her to know about *The Lady from Brazil*, I said sternly.

"Then you don't want me to mention my duets with Mrs. Lancaster," Mrs. Bedlington said coyly.

I could remember no discussion of duets, because—much as I had wanted the apartment—the last thing I needed would have been for her to confront Burt with that.

"No, I don't want her getting *any* ideas about acting. It must remain strictly our secret," I said. "There's only one lady from Brazil, and I think you know who I mean."

If I had any intention of mentioning Mrs. Bedlington, which I doubt, it vanished once I caught sight of the dinner table. There were lighted candles, flowers, peaked napkins, sparkling champagne glasses—everything required to mark a festive occasion. Mike not only had a different wine for every course, but he threw in a lot of extra bows besides. Rita said she had never eaten better in any restaurant. Inscrutability notwithstanding, Mike couldn't hide his pleasure.

Her compliment set the tone for the entire dinner. I know I couldn't quit talking about the Coquilles St. Jacques.

"Have you always liked fish that much?"

I had to think. "No, I can't remember eating any until we moved from St. Louis to Seattle."

"It's usually because your parents like something that you do," she said. "Have you found that to be true?"

"Absolutely true," I said, smiling. Rita, I'd discovered, could give even a grand master lessons in the oblique approach.

"What about oysters?"

That made me grin. "My father brought some home in the shell. I guess I was about eleven. He took one out with a fork and held it up. It was the ugliest critter I'd ever seen. Then he dropped it into his mouth and swallowed it. We thought it was the bravest thing we'd ever seen.

"We asked my mother how he'd managed it.

"My mother laughed. 'It comes with a college degree,' she said."

"Where'd he go to school?" Rita asked.

"He got his law degree from Michigan."

"What's he like, when he's not swallowing oysters?"

"I guess he's no different from other fathers," I said.

"Yes, he's different, or you wouldn't be able to say that so easily," she said.

"What about your father? What's he like?" I asked.

"Let's talk about him another time," she said. "Where'd your father's family come from?"

I knew an evasive maneuver when I met one. "I don't know where my grandfather came from. I just know that there were these five sisters from Virginia. Their father gave each of them one hundred acres of land in Illinois when they married. So my grandfather, who couldn't read or write, was a farmer. And that was where my father grew up. On that hundred-acre farm."

"What do you think about when you think of him?"

"I don't know," I said, because I had never thought about it before. "What do you think about?"

"Someone stern. A disciplinarian."

"And your mother?"

"She was the opposite," Rita said. "Very gentle."

At least I had gotten a reaction. But before I could probe any further, I saw that she had thought of something. "I once read an aphorism that I loved. 'The true index of a man's character is the health of his wife.' "

"Do you believe those things?"

"Sometimes."

"My mother's the healthiest member of our family," I said. "So the old man should be proud of himself."

"Is your father strict?"

"We always wanted to please him. In the whole world, I wanted to please him more than anyone else. So he didn't *have* to be strict."

"What about your mother?"

I had to chuckle. "There was nothing I did that didn't please her."

Rita seemed preoccupied. Then she said something that really surprised me. "I just hope they like me. Do you think they will?"

"You mean all this probing was because you're worried about that?"

"I'd like to invite them to dinner," she said.

"What about your father?"

"Let's just have your folks over this first time."

I shook my head—all that circumlocution to arrive at a family get-together. "If you're worried about their liking you, I'll give you two keys. With the old man, ask him if he's interested in a hooker as you're putting a bottle of bourbon out. With my mother, just tell her you'd like to see her scrapbook."

"If she keeps a scrapbook," Rita said, "I'll bet she also has a baby album."

"Ohmigod!" I cried, catching myself. "That's exactly what she'll do. She'll get that baby album out. Promise me you won't bring that up. Promise!"

Rita just smiled enigmatically. "You don't mind if I invite them, do you?"

"Nothing could make me happier," I said.

It was a roundabout way of finding out about someone, but I figured if I talked enough about me and my family, it was just a matter of living into the next century—or maybe the one after that—until I knew everything there was to know about her and her family.

Rita tapped the table with her fist. "That's the very first thing we'll do when I get back from San Francisco. We'll have your parents to dinner. And for the first course, Coquilles St. Jacques."

She picked up her brandy, so I picked up mine and followed her into the den. I found I did a lot of that blissful following in the cave. Clearly, this was Rita's night for plans. She sat at the desk, put on her glasses, took out a pad and pen, then got going on our trip to Pebble Beach. When someone has that exotic mixture of Spanish and Irish blood, and they get up that sort of a head of steam, I found the safest bet was to settle back for the ride.

She made a list of all the things we shouldn't take, but would be more fun if we did—our favorite bathrobes, vodka, soap, Dom Perignon, and things to eat. With her that meant caviar; with me, raw peanuts.

Then she had me make a list of things we couldn't afford *not* to take, or there would be no reason to make the trip. That included her paints, brushes, and canvases; my paper, pencils, and something she had discovered in one of the closets. An electric pencil sharpener.

"I don't know why you had that hidden away," she said, plugging it in to make sure it worked. "This is something you're *really* going to need."

"It wasn't that I hid it away," I explained. "I only bring it out when I want to sharpen up my wits, not my pencils."

She didn't smile. She was that serious about what we were doing.

The last list was of the various golf courses up there. Then we had to decide on the two we'd rather play. Since we planned leaving on a Friday and returning Sunday, and since it took a day driving up and the same coming back, it was going to be a problem getting all that golf in—plus painting, and writing, and maybe a hug or two, if I was lucky.

"I wonder if we shouldn't limit our golf to one round," I said, when we were having trouble deciding on a second course. She frowned, so I added quickly, "So we won't neglect the painting and writing, I mean."

She immediately looked relieved. "That's good thinking. If we're only going to play one round, then it will have to be Pebble Beach."

She still had the packing to do. Mike could have done it for her, but she had to let him go home as soon as he had finished up in the kitchen. I was beginning to get weary myself, so I have no idea where she found that boundless energy. Between us, we managed to get everything into the two suitcases, except for one last item.

It was a pair of castanets. The way she picked them up told me why they were the last thing packed. It was like watching a great pool player pick up and fondle his cue.

I once asked Sam Snead's caddy what he liked most about him on the course. "Everything, he said. "He looks beautiful just taking a club out of the bag."

That was Rita with those castanets. I would have loved to ask her to play them, because they had always fascinated me. But the hour was late, and the studio limousine was calling for her before dawn.

She rubbed them, turned them this way and that, and as intently as I was watching her, I never saw her slip her fingers into them. But the next thing—with the slightest of movement on the part of those slender fingers of hers—she began to make them come alive. Utterly oblivious to me, she kicked off her shoes and began to dance.

I knew I was watching something special. It wasn't just her grace, or the story she was narrating with those castanets. I couldn't put my finger on exactly what made it unique. But one thing I was sure of, it was like nothing I had ever seen her do on the screen.

Most superstars are a reflection of their personality. I mean, Gary Cooper plays Gary Cooper. He is the same off the screen as on it. But there was nothing of the Love Goddess, or Gilda, or the Lady from Shanghai in what she was doing. This wasn't Rita Hayworth, so she had to be Margarita Cansino.

It wasn't until she finished that I realized she had done the entire dance without music. I found myself applauding wildly. She had forgotten me completely, but that brought a tiny smile.

"I thought I knew you, but I never knew anything like that was inside you," I said. "If I had a wish, that's what I'd wish. That I could do something like that."

I was in such a state of excitement I couldn't stop raving, even though I should have known how embarrassed she got with such outright praise. So I was barely aware of the three simple steps she showed me, until I had gone over them a couple of times. Then she put a tape on the stereo, and while I did whichever one of those three steps she cued me into, she danced all around me.

It had always puzzled me how people who had never danced before looked so great, once they worked with Fred Astaire. Well, now I knew. I could see us in the mirrors on the wall.

Of all my fantasies, the favorite was the one where I had this unbelievably beautiful dancing partner and we did the old soft shoe at the Palace, or wherever they still did the old soft shoe. I'd be sporting a straw hat, which I'd spin off my head from time to time and run up and down my arm. I never envisioned it coming true, or the one thing that would make it superior to any soft shoe ever done before. I mean I not only would have the unbelievably beautiful girl —but castanets.

In looking back on that night, I realize it was the last time we accepted each other just for what we were. We weren't trying to make each other into something different. So why change it? That's what I'm sitting here asking myself.

In all this time nothing had been said about us. Not a whisper of our relationship, although newspapers, magazines, and newscasts chronicled her every move from the time she arrived at the studio until she left at the end of the day. They were forever mentioning how she rode in a big Lincoln Continental with a Japanese chauffeur. Since I traveled up front with Mike, I guess they figured I was her footman.

It wasn't until the third day after she had gone to San Francisco, which meant I was eating my third straight dinner alone, that I became aware the phone never rang. If nobody knew about us, then what had happened to the girls I'd been going out with before Rita?

Not that I was really interested, but a couple of them actually had figured I might marry them. So not hearing from them was a blessing, but it still mystified me. That was how I came to call one of them right after I ate my third dinner alone.

I intended telling her I had been working nights, which was why she hadn't heard from me. That would give her a chance to tell me why I hadn't heard from her. If she sounded too depressed, since she was one of those who figured on marrying me, I figured I might drop by for a martini. She made great martinis with Bombay gin.

Of course, after we had a martini or two, I'd have to tell her why I wouldn't be able to phone her again, since I was all tied up with someone else. Not only would that keep her from getting any ideas, but it would wipe the slate clean once and for all.

Only after she answered the phone, I had no more than said hello, when her voice began dripping icicles. She said I had some nerve calling—that she'd never guessed what I was really like, but now she knew. And with that she hung up.

When I got the same reception from a second girl, I was more than mystified, I was baffled. The one person I hadn't heard from was Dorothy Dumont. So rather than risk another disastrous phone conversation, I decided just to drop by at the address listed for her in the phone book.

It wasn't until I was approaching her apartment building that I realized that, since Rita, I had never in my life been happier than I was now. So why not leave well enough alone. Not slowing down as I passed Dorothy's building gave me a larger-than-life feeling. I knew Rita would probably never know of my gesture, but never again would she have a phone call to worry about. I *had* wiped the slate clean.

On the way home, I picked up a gallon of sake. I had never had a drink with Mike, so I didn't know what he liked, but I decided that was how I would spend the evenings until Rita returned. I'd have a couple of hot sakes with old Mike, and then I'd take him out to dinner for a change.

I used the stairway route to avoid a chance encounter with Mrs. Bedlington, which brought me into my apartment from the rear. No sooner was I inside than I heard low laughter from the living room. It was Dorothy. I could tell from the tone of Mike's voice that she already had him cavorting in the palm of her hand.

My first instinct was to ease back out and not return until she had gone. But I felt so righteous, I decided to step into my parlor. I was glad I did, because the first thing I got was the answer to the riddle.

"Of course, I called," Dorothy said when I asked where she'd been.

"After you walked out on me the night of your New Year's Eve party, I must have called half a dozen times over the next few days."

"I sometimes put the phones away so that I can't hear them," I explained. I knew the time she was referring to—those first unforgettable days in the cave.

"It was at least another week before I tried again," Dorothy said. "Then I got this voice that spoke in broken English."

"Mike?"

"No, no, it was a woman's voice."

"It was?"

"Yes, it was," she said irritably. "So I said, is this the Hill residence? The voice said it was. Then I said, Who am I speaking to? There was a pause, then the voice said, 'Close friend.' I said, 'How close?' The voice said, 'Mistress.' "

"Mistress?" I said.

"Don't look so surprised."

"What did you say then?"

"I hung up."

I burst out laughing. No *wonder* the others had slammed the phone down. Dorothy never lost her stony expression. She went on to say it was days before the voice finally registered. She had been around it on so many pictures, that in spite of the accent, she finally realized it was Rita's. So when she read in the papers that Rita had gone to San Francisco, she came on over.

"Do you think she recognized your voice?" I said.

"It wouldn't be like Rita to be that interested."

"She never mentioned the call," I said. "I just know the phones stopped ringing."

That made Dorothy chuckle. "I admire your taste," she said.

Of all the girls I've ever met, Dorothy was the only one who gave full credit to the competition. She hadn't a trace of envy in her makeup. I hadn't planned on it, but I found myself pouring us a drink.

"You should have called me at the office," I told her.

"I did," she said. "But with Rita in your life, I can see why that guru of yours never put me through."

"Ted."

"The big Buddha. I met him the night of your party," she said. "After two calls to your office, I tried to make it clear that I was interested in your mind at the moment, not your body."

"Well, you're here, and you've got it."

"Biddy Lieding," she said. "Does that ring a bell?"

I hadn't heard her name since college, yet even after all those years, it instantly summoned the memory of the girl who wore the most expensive fur on the University of Washington campus. My first love, Biddy Lieding.

No matter how wet and cold it got on those rainy Seattle nights, that great white fur of hers was like traveling with your own private igloo—if you can imagine an igloo that attractive, and being lucky enough to get invited inside. Now with all that going for her, she didn't need to be the only daughter of the richest man in the Northwest, but Biddy had that distinction, too.

According to Dorothy, Biddy's father had died and left her all his millions. She had decided her one ambition was to break into the movie business. As Dorothy said, you don't have to have talent to make movies, as long as you're backing someone who does. Biddy had been making inquiries about me when Dorothy met her. I could see how those wheels of Dorothy's had started spinning.

"That was why I've been so anxious to talk to you," Dorothy said. "With her kind of money, it's a chance to form your own company."

"What about the lady who answers my phone?"

"What about her?"

"Would she be interested in such a partnership?" I said. "I doubt it."

Dorothy sipped her drink, studying me over the rim. "You haven't been listening."

"Not really," I said. "I can't get over Rita."

"I can see that."

"I mean, I can't get over what she did to you on the telephone," I said. "She always seem so shy and helpless."

"She really has got her claws into you, hasn't she?"

I had to smile. "She never had much choice."

"She had a choice," Dorothy said, and she said it emphatically. "Rita gets what she wants. I remember the first time I watched her work. It was on *Gilda*. During rehearsals, she spoke so low it was hard to hear her."

"She always speaks softly."

"Not on the first take. She was clear and letter-perfect. But then the director decided he wanted something different. Well, she was never that clear or letter-perfect again. So after ten more takes, the director told her to try it again the way she did it the first time. She did, and they printed it, and that was the way it was in the finished picture."

It made me shake my head in admiration. "Hard to believe."

"I know," Dorothy said. "I've stood in for her, and I've worked on sets with her. The voice may be soft, but there's steel underneath."

Dorothy was wise not to press Biddy Lieding and her money any further, but I sensed I hadn't heard the last of it. So we finished our drinks, and I had Mike drive her home.

When Mike got perturbed, he always sucked air in when he talked instead of letting it out. That was what he was doing as he told me that he thought it had been Miss Hayworth on the phone, but she had hung up.

The clock beside my bed read 5:20, which meant the sun hadn't bothered to get up yet. So while I put on a robe from the closet, I told Mike to go back to the beginning.

"Hello, I say," Mike said, nervously recapitulating. " 'Hello,' other voice say. I think other voice nice girl from last night, so I say, 'No sooner take you home, than you already call back.' " Mike paused, but when he spoke again, he started sucking in air. "Phone go click in ear. Other voice hang up. I hang up. Think. Not nice girl from last night. No way."

"That's all?" I said.

Mike's eyes got even narrower, which was hard to do when you're already Japanese. "Was Miss Hayworth."

The look on his face, and the way he was frantically sucking in air and all really made me laugh. "I told you, Mike, you weren't opening the car door often enough for her."

That made him look so sad that I took the time to explain Miss

Hayworth, since I didn't have anything else to do at that hour anyway. Also, it never hurts to reassure yourself.

In dealing with the Oriental mind, I realized the importance of putting him at ease, which was why I reminded him right off that Miss Hayworth was in San Francisco making a motion picture. Since she happened to be one of the screen's greatest stars, it meant she had more important things to do than put through a call at this hour simply to hang up on him.

This seemed to relax him, so I went on to explain how Miss Hayworth had a man's mind, since she had grown up in a man's world. I even went all the way back to that first time when I saw her in Tijuana, where she was already making a living for her family, when she couldn't have been over thirteen.

It's funny, but I don't think I realized then how much I missed her, which was why I couldn't stop talking about her. It wasn't until he was driving me to work that I finally wound it all up by telling Mike how anyone with such a superior mind would never have hung up on him. She was far too well-mannered. And if he thought she might have been affected by anything he said on the phone, I advised him to forget it. She was just too superior a lady.

That afternoon a curious phone call came to my office from Mike. He was sucking in air like he intended to pull me right through the receiver.

"Superior lady back," Mike hissed. "Windows going fast."

"Windows going fast" had me puzzled, until I heard this tinkling of breaking glass over the phone.

"What was that?" I said.

"Windows going fast," Mike hissed.

It's funny how you can know something is happening, but still can't make yourself believe it. "You mean Miss Hayworth's back?"

There was another tinkling of glass, followed by some more hyperventilation by old Mike. "Windows going fast."

"Did you forget to open the car door for her or anything?"

"No doors," Mike hissed. "Just windows."

Then there was an even bigger crash, and then the line went dead. By a sublime accident of chance, at the same time the windows

were going fast, I had been arranging a midafternoon tea in my office.
It was to be sort of a trial run—with cucumber sandwiches, and
scones, and all the fixings—so when Rita got back from San Fran-
cisco, we'd have the real tea. And I'd invite Burt and Norma, since I
hadn't even let him know how much we had come to like each other.
I didn't want my best friends reading about it in the newspapers first.
So if this trial run worked out, I might even invite more than just
Burt and Norma.

Ted was out picking up the cucumber sandwiches when Mike's
call came in, so I waited for him by the curb. With the windows
going fast like that, there was no time to summon a taxi. As soon as
Ted drove up, I had him head right for my apartment.

I had just about decided on a course of action. I knew instinctively
that no matter how innocent the evening with Dorothy had been,
there was no way to explain it. Especially after the phone call that
Rita had intercepted. A delicate misunderstanding was like quicksand
—the more you struggled to get out of it, the deeper in you sank. So
I somehow had to make her understand that whoever had been there,
hadn't been there by invitation.

With Ted worrying so vocally about the cucumber sandwiches
drying out, I decided to try to divert him with my proposed strategy.
I told him about Mike's getting the phone call, but that it was hard
for me to believe his mere mention of having taken an anonymous
girl home could have triggered Rita's return from San Francisco in
the middle of a picture.

Then I spelled out my concern for her concern, because Ted was
a man who liked harmony. Especially in the lives of the people he
worked for.

"How do you plan on alleviating her concern?"

"With the truth," I said. "Naturally."

Ted looked relieved. "I'm glad."

"If there was a woman at my place last night, she was there to see
Mike, not me," I said.

Ted looked aghast. "But Mike's a happily married man—with children."

I leaned closer to Ted and lowered my voice. "Maybe, just maybe
he's a happily married man," I said.

"What do you mean?"

"Have you ever noticed how he sometimes sucks in air when he's talking?" I said.

"Yes, I have."

"It's an old Japanese cover-up. His way of making you *think* he's happy at home."

Ted frowned and pursed his lips. When you're a Buddha look-alike, it's a way of showing your terrible disappointment in someone you're always trying to look up to—something Ted worked hard at with me.

It really got to me, because we were getting closer and closer to my apartment, and Rita just happened to think the world of Ted. It was important to have him on my side.

"Believe me, Ted, I never invited anyone over to the apartment last night," I said.

Ted got to looking even sterner. "You told me you made a vow never to lie in Miss Hayworth's presence."

"I'll swear on the Bible," I said. "I never invited anyone over."

Ted gave that some thought, then he visibly relaxed. "I believe you," he said.

I figured I had Ted solidly in my corner, when he turned pale. Then his mouth dropped open, as he struggled to say something but couldn't. I followed his gaze up to the windows in my apartment.

When I say windows, I'm talking about a stretch of glass panels in my living room on the third floor that extended half the length of a football field. Except there *weren't* any windows. I mean, if you want to be technical, there was one still left where the glass was only cracked.

So I said to Ted, as casually as I could, that it would be a good idea for him to bring up the tray of cucumber sandwiches. I reminded him of how Rita loved them. It was no time for losing the only ally I had, but I did. Ted never even pretended to get out from behind the wheel. He just said he'd remembered he had to get right back to the office because he was already late for a meeting with Burt.

I didn't blame him too much for being such a coward after seeing all those broken windows, but I can't stand a lousy liar. Especially one who makes such a to-do about someone else's lying. Anyway, I took the tray out of the back of his car, and just so he'd feel guilty for deserting me, I gave him a couple of the sandwiches to eat on his way back to the office.

If you've got to face something alone, and you're not all that sure about it, the key is to keep it light. I kept reminding myself on the stairs that if I had done something wrong, it would be another story. But I hadn't.

The iron gate stood open; so did the front door. In the gathering dusk, she was lighting this big Mexican candelabra that stood on the floor. She looked as beautiful as ever, and just as fragile and defenseless. She must have felt me standing there, because she looked over.

I hadn't put the tray of cucumber sandwiches down, hoping she might notice them. Since she never ate on the plane, I figured she might even thank me for being so thoughtful. But she didn't. So I put the tray down.

"You're back early," I said. That wasn't exactly what I meant by keeping it light, but I had to begin somewhere.

"Yes."

She said that word so softly it made everything very, very still, and I liked that. It meant she was back.

"Mike thought he might have offended you on the phone."

"No, but it was talking with him that made me decide to come back."

"I see."

It was like we were total strangers. So what I did, which was the best thing I could come up with to bring a little warmth back into a room where there was none—and I'm not referring to the broken windows—was to mix up a batch of martinis.

"Mike said he'd mentioned some girl to you on the phone. He mistook your voice for hers," I said casually. "I think he said she had come over to visit him earlier."

"He did mention a girl."

I handed her a martini. "Did he suck in air? I mean old Mike, when he mentioned the girl?"

"I don't recall."

"Then he probably didn't," I said, but I said it so it sounded as if he probably did.

Rita frowned. "Should he have?"

Now I had her interest, so it made it possible to move a lot closer. I had to pretend I didn't want old Mike to hear, even though I knew he was hiding in the kitchen, which made him no braver than Ted. If you want to talk about oversized cowards—and all because of this soft-spoken 115-pounder—I was surrounded by them.

"I don't want this to go any further," I said, and I almost lost my train of thought. I had gotten so close that I could catch the nifty aroma that was always a part of her. "But I think he's interested in some girl." This caused Rita to frown even more. "For God's sake, don't say anything."

"No."

"If he starts hyperventilating, just ignore it," I warned.

"I will."

"I don't think he's too happy at home."

"Is that why he's hyperventilating?"

I nodded, and risked another step closer, as I dropped my voice. "He's Japanese, you know."

"But aren't the Japanese the same as everyone else, except for their eyes?"

"Yes," I said, "but only the Japanese make a big thing of it. I mean hyperventilation when they're troubled like he is."

"You never met the girl?"

"No."

"Maybe his problem is simpler than you think."

"Oh . . . ?"

"Maybe he doesn't open the car door for her."

That was what I meant about keeping it light. Her words were like a ray of sunshine in the rain. She wasn't smiling, but there was no mistaking the glint of humor in her eyes. I figured I had only to play my final card to ensure a more relaxed future for the two of us.

"It's those little things that loom so large when there's no honest communication between two people," I said. "I hope you won't feel I betrayed a confidence, but I told Mike of your sophisticated outlook on life. So if his marriage has run into trouble, so that he had to look for solace in another girl, you'd be the first to understand."

"I'm glad you reassured him."

"I even went further, using myself as an example," I confessed. "I told him that while I couldn't imagine having an occasion to stray, there was nothing Miss Hayworth wouldn't be big enough to overlook." When she didn't immediately concur, but stared at me over the rim of her glass, I was quick to add, "If she knew it was working toward a better understanding between us, that is."

"I beg your pardon."

It was the way she said that, *very* aloof, that threw me.

"I said," pausing to add a smile, because I was suddenly conscious that the glint of humor had left her eye, "I said there was nothing I did in my outside life that you weren't big enough to overlook."

"You could be wrong."

It was almost like my voice was changing, I was that startled. "I could . . . ?"

"Yes."

In an effort to get things light again, I pretended to feel a chill. So without making a direct reference to all the broken windows, I began rubbing my hands together.

"I don't know about you, but I feel a draft in here," I said.

"Maybe we should have a fire."

She was being very tight-lipped. To avoid her gaze, I moved to the thermostat. "It's broken," I said as I worked it up and down. "We can't have heat if we can't get the temperature down lower."

She just stared at me. I noticed that window, the only one still unbroken. So I had to make this last feeble attempt at keeping things light.

"Maybe it's that one window that's keeping the temperature up," I said. "Maybe if it was open like the rest, maybe that would do it."

She never changed expression, just picked up a golf club that was leaning against the wall. Then she separated one ball with it from several that were lying there, satisfying my curiosity as to how she had broken the windows.

If you've ever tried to punch a three iron to keep it low, you know how you've got to play the ball back in your stance, and make sure not to rush your swing. It really takes an expert to bring off the shot.

Well, Rita was an expert, because she put that ball right through the center of the one remaining window. It made me shudder, hearing all that glass tinkle to the sidewalk below, even though I had to admire her execution.

"Now can we have a fire?" she said, in that soft, soft voice.

I no sooner had a roaring fire going, than Mrs. Bedlington Four stormed into the living room with her Pekingese in her arms. She didn't even bother to sound the chimes or anything, she was that furious.

Everything was in shadow. The only light was from the fire and a single candle, which was why she wasn't aware of Rita. So when she heard this light laugh behind her, Mrs. Bedlington whirled.

Everything seemed to shudder under her armor as recognition dawned, and with it a terrible sense of betrayal. She shot her head forward for a closer inspection, stretching her neck something fierce, and she dropped the Peke. It landed on its head, but she never heard its outraged cry, or was aware of its tearing out the front door. She was that transfixed. But only briefly. Then she started yelling.

Mostly about how she had always been proud of this address, because it was considered one of the classiest in the city. Its reputation impeccable. Now to discover that my live-in maid *lived in*—and wasn't even my niece, but Rita Hayworth, who had nothing better to do in her wanton way than to help me knock out windows—was the last straw.

"I want you out!" Mrs. Bedlington screamed. "Out! Out! Out!"

Rita winced, unused to such stridency, and looked toward me to do something. Although I didn't have a *long* cigarette holder, I lit up a cigarette as though I did.

"*Mrs.* Bedlington," I addressed her, using my loftiest voice, "there's one thing I'd like to get straight first. Miss Hayworth did *not* help me knock out those windows. She did it all by herself. I didn't even tee up the golf balls for her."

Mrs. Bedlington had turned a curious shade of puce, but she was listening, so I continued.

"Like the flame on that candle, Mrs. Bedlington. One day when you're least expecting it, your head will go just as quickly as that flame. And while I'd like to wrap my fingers around your neck, so your head is teed up real nice for Miss Hayworth, she won't need that, because she's splendid on her own."

Whooooosh! The club in Rita's slender fingers slashed through the air and out went the flame atop that great big candle in that great big candelabra. It was the last thing I'd expected from anyone as slight and feminine as Rita, which made it about fifty times as scary in the eerie half light from the fireplace.

Mrs. Bedlington's hands shot to her head, where she clapped them to her ears.

"No more flame, Mrs. Bedlington," I said, soft and solemn. "It's out, out, out!"

Mrs. Bedlington gave a piercing scream and fled.

If we had rehearsed that routine every day for a month, we couldn't have worked better as a team. So naturally, when you bring one off like that, you expect something in the way of a reward. My expectations were modest. I was willing to settle for a hug. One tiny, teeny, little hug.

Only I failed to get even that, because Rita still had this glazed, unseeing look as though I wasn't there. I had only seen a look like that once before. It was during the war, on a machine gunner carrying a Browning automatic who had just wiped out an entire pocket of the enemy.

Now while Rita didn't have a Browning, she still had that golf club in her hand, and she suddenly brought it back in this fierce way, like she was about to extinguish another flame, or maybe an entire pocket.

Luckily, I looked up in time to see two elderly people standing in the doorway. A man and a woman. "No, no," I cried. "They're our friends."

"How do *you* know?" Rita said in this new and deadly voice, her steely gaze never wavering.

"I grew up with them," I said. "They're my parents."

Slowly, she lowered her Browning, and the old look of wariness returned to her eyes. It was something I had noticed when she was around Mike at first, or anyone else new for that matter. She would go into her shell, and most of the time she would never bother to come back out.

Only this night, she suddenly smiled, and it was like the rainbow after the storm. I could tell my folks had sensed that momentary withdrawal on her part, so her smile brought an answering one from them.

"I'm Rita Hayworth," she said, as if they had no idea who she might be. "I dropped by, because your son is having trouble with his landlord."

"That was his landlord?" my mother said. "That woman who just flew by?"

Rita nodded, a very serious nod. She also lowered her voice. "I don't think he pays his rent."

There was no one like her when she wanted to be charming; no one I've ever met before or since.

My father brought forth this outsized jug of Irish whiskey from the sack he was carrying. "We picked this up in our travels, so we'd have something to fortify us against just such embarrassments."

"I didn't expect you back for another day or two," I said. "We've been planning a dinner. Rita was anxious to meet you."

"Well, we've met, so how about a hooker?"

I took the jug of whiskey from him and led the way to the bar. Rita fell in beside my mother.

"What am I going to *do* about your son?" Rita said to her.

"Are you in love with him?"

Rita frowned, pretending to think. "I'm not sure."

"Then you still have time to run for your life."

Rita turned to the old man. "What do you think?"

"I always agree with his mother," my father said, "until I've buried that first hooker."

I had set out some shot glasses, along with his favorite bourbon, so that was Rita's cue to step up and pour. The old man raised his glass to her, then they downed their drinks. Unlike me, Rita neither shuddered, nor batted an eye, and don't think the old man's face didn't light up at that.

"Risk it," he said.

My mother clucked her disapproval. She had a tall drink, which she sipped at, since one drink lasted her an evening. Rita pretended to think some more.

"Maybe if I knew more about him," Rita said, "maybe then it would be easier to make up my mind."

My mother smiled her approval. "We'll start with his scrapbook." Then suddenly her face lit up. "No, I have a better idea. We'll start with his baby album."

"You promised," I said to Rita. Then I appealed to both parents. "She promised she wouldn't get into that."

"I don't know why he has this thing about his baby album," Rita said.

My mother looked thoughtful. "I do. It shows how much he has to hide. He was doing things at three weeks that you should know about."

It was hard to believe this was the same girl who had knocked out all those windows. The transition had been seamless. She had remembered the two keys. First, the hooker; then, the baby album. And the next thing, she was sitting off to one side with my mother, talking as if they had known each other forever.

"Where did she find you?" my father said.

"She didn't. I found her."

"I see."

It was his theory that no man ever found a woman, unless the woman had planned it that way. So when he said, "I see," he made no effort to hide his smile.

"Where's she from?"

"She was born in New York, but grew up out here," I said.

"Once your mother gets me home, she's going to ask me what we talked about. But what she'll really be asking is Why didn't I find out something about Rita?" He caught me smiling. "What's amusing?"

"It was just last week that Rita was asking me the same thing about you two," I said.

"You read so much about her—then you meet her and she's anything but what you've read," he said. "I guess it would help if we went to more movies."

I wasn't about to start kidding him, but I knew the only picture they had seen in the last ten years was a second run of *The Pride of the Yankees*.

Anyway, I filled him in on Rita's father being Spanish, and her mother Irish, and the fact she had two brothers and all of that, but I could see he was only half listening.

"What I really hoped was that you'd give me some idea of what your mother and I have to offer that would interest her," he said.

"Just yourselves. She doesn't make friends," I told him. "I have a feeling you'd be good for her."

It was about then that Mike made an appearance. "Mr. Harry Cohn would like to speak to Miss Hayworth."

I don't know how he had been able to track her down, but when you're Harry Cohn, with a network of spies at your command, there's not much you can't do. The call had to be about her walking off the picture in San Francisco. After all the months we'd spent wracking our brains over how to get her out of that contract, this could only make it worse.

"Why don't you tell Mike you'll call him back?" I suggested. That would give us a chance to talk over her strategy.

Right away, the folks insisted they had to go, saying they had already overstayed. So I told Rita I would see them to their car, and be right back.

She did something then I had never seen her do before. She gave each of them a peck on the cheek. I mean, she just didn't kiss people, or call everybody darling, or all that other crap that was so much a part of our trade.

Once my mother was behind the wheel, she got very serious. "You see that girl gets some rest," she said. "And you get some, too."

Rita was in the den when I got back to the apartment. She looked a million miles away. She was huddled in a chair, as if she were freezing. I knew she must be thinking about Cohn.

"The reason I wanted you to wait and call Cohn back was to review what you're going to say." When she didn't answer, I moved closer to her chair. "I thought about him all the way down and all the way back up. I decided you should let him steam. Unless you think there's some way he can make things too tough. Otherwise, I know we can lick him."

It was a long moment before she turned to me. I had the feeling she'd forgotten I was there. Then she did something totally unexpected. She gave me a hug. But it wasn't like any other hug. Not the way she clung to me. It was as though if she let go, her world might go, too.

I don't know how long that hug might have lasted if the chimes hadn't sounded. I would cheerfully have ignored them, but then we heard voices, so Rita decided I should see what was going on.

It was turning into a night for unexpected visitors. Who stood on the doorstep, but the police. And not just one squad car's worth, but two, which should give some idea of the picture painted by Mrs. Bedlington.

They were all edging past Mike into the living room, moving cautiously like the place was mined or concealed desperate characters. One big Irish sergeant, who seemed to be the head of the group, presented the collected injuries of Mrs. Bedlington Four. She had filed a complaint, asserting that she'd had to flee the very premises she owned because of general mayhem, an excess of broken windows, and dark threats to her person. Rita was nowhere in sight.

Anyway, the way the sergeant talked while he inspected each broken window, I was ripe for shipment to Siberia, or a firing squad, or worse. Finally, I thought, he would settle on taking me for a ride down to the police station.

I was worrying about what to tell Mike to tell Rita in order not to upset her, when she suddenly appeared. The sergeant was the first to notice. Obviously, Mrs. Bedlington hadn't included Rita in her complaint. You could tell by his look. When his troops saw that dumbstruck look on their leader, they all whirled—and discovered Rita Hayworth.

No one can imagine the impact Rita had on grown men. As used to her and her ways as I'd become, even I never got used to it. It didn't take so much as a smile, just her presence, and they were ready to fall at her feet. So when she did smile, they toppled like dominoes.

"I was hoping someone would drop in," she said, "and join me in a cup of Irish tea."

She always liked a cup of tea before she went to bed, only tonight, I could see her eye was on the oversized jug of Irish whiskey my old man had brought, so I made a beeline for the kitchen, where I had Mike get busy brewing the tea.

One thing about tea—it becomes infinitely more drinkable when there's some Irish whiskey in the cup. Then when she started passing around that tray of tiny cucumber tea sandwiches, it was like she was entertaining the L.A.P.D.'s gay rights squad. They were all working so hard at being sophisticated—some of them even had their pinkies extended.

When I said she had them all under her spell, I was exaggerating by one. I'm referring to the sergeant, who got to looking progressively more righteous, the more his men drank Irish tea. But Rita had him in her sights. She started fingering those castanets of hers, and the next thing we knew she had drawn him into a sultry tango.

What made that tango a real eye-opener for me though was her makeup. I hadn't noticed her slip away, so she couldn't have been gone more than a minute, but she'd made up one side of her face as a black, and the other side white. It was incredible the way she could vary her dance style, depending on which side of her face was showing. In one breath she'd be a lush, sensuous Creole dancer out of the New Orleans Mardi Gras, and in the next, she'd be a snooty Park Avenue belle.

I got a prickly feeling as the full significance of the story she was telling started sinking in. She was imitating Dorothy Dumont. I'm talking about Dorothy passing as white. She had all Dorothy's gestures unnervingly right.

No wonder the great moviemakers came out of the silents. I never realized how much could be said without words. And that bemused buffalo of a sergeant was moving blissfully around as if he was the niftiest thing on two feet.

I guess that's when it hit me. In the story she was telling, the dumb sergeant was clearly me. Talk about your shock of recognition!

Anyway, she finally gave me a glance, and I guess I must have let my feeling show, because she sure looked satisfied with herself.

What followed was the turning point in our relationship. Looking back, I'd say it was the turning point in my whole life, although at first it didn't seem all that significant.

It started with her beginning to make fun of the whole story she had just told—to burlesque it. She went from Charlie Chaplin to W. C. Fields to Mae West and back to Charlie Chaplin. If there's anything comparable to what I felt then, it would have to be the thrill

of the baseball scout who drops by a sandlot game and finds himself
watching this kid with the blazing fast ball who turns into the future
Babe Ruth. Or Diaghilev, when he got his first glimpse of this young
fellow Nijinsky, who seemed to jump right off the stage and through
the roof.

In the history of the movie business there have only been one or
two beautiful women with a true comedic talent. There was just no
doubt about it, I was watching something as rare as a ruby—one of
the great beauties of our time with a comic gift to match. And she
was part of me—part of this new world I was sharing. I can't begin
to tell you the intense excitement I felt at that moment.

Anyway, when the police took their leave, I watched that big
sergeant fall all over himself—he was that infatuated. He told Rita if
she should ever have another problem with the landlady, just to call
him, and he'd see that he and his men ran her right out of town. And
as long as we stayed in that apartment, we never heard another peep
out of Mrs. Bedlington Four.

Since Mike had left earlier, Rita and I were tidying up. That was
somehow the best part of the night for me, because I always got to
thinking back to those years before she came when I'd be out walking
alone. And how much I'd envy couples I'd see through lighted windows helping each other. Or even if they weren't helping each other
—as long as they weren't belting each other—I always envied their
having each other.

But there was one thing that was still bothering me. When she'd
give me that special hug, I'd sort of taken for granted it was her way
of telling me she'd decided that if there *had* been a girl here while she
was up in San Francisco, she hadn't been by invitation.

But then when she did the dance; she not only made it plain she
knew there'd been a girl—and that the girl was Dorothy—but she
made it even plainer that I hadn't fooled her for a minute. Then why
did I get that hug?

I'd been keeping an eye on her, because she was weaving a little,
which wasn't surprising when I thought back over her long day, and
the way she had finished it off with all that Irish tea.

Anyway, I waited until she'd collapsed onto the sofa. "I'm still
trying to figure why I was lucky enough to get that hug."

"It was the wonderful feeling I had after I hung up on Harry Cohn," she said.

I couldn't believe I'd heard right. "You talked to Harry Cohn?"

"Not at first. I listened until I managed to get a word in. Then I made it very plain to Harry. I told him I had found something more important in life than his movie."

"When did you realize that?"

"When your folks were here."

My face must have mirrored my delight, because she started to giggle. I had never heard her giggle before. It was like opening a music box; she was a little girl again.

"I told Harry I had no intention of coming back to the picture, since I had no intention of making any more pictures. Once he stopped screaming and swearing, he began to realize I was serious. Then he said that if I'd finish the picture, he would let me out of the rest of my contract." She was that proud. "I wanted to do it on my own. That was why I called him while you were seeing your folks to their car."

No wonder she had drunk so much Irish tea and danced the way she had—no wonder she captivated me and the sergeant, and the troops. It's a wonder she hadn't gone right through the roof, after all those years of being tied to that studio. After all those long years of having to do whatever Cohn said, if she wanted to work. Then to suddenly have the courage to say no—I swear I've never felt so good for anyone.

"My mother said you're not getting enough sleep."

"Neither are you," she shot back. "Now it's my turn to ask you a question. When I was in San Francisco, did you begin to ask yourself, What am I getting into?"

"What made you think that?"

"Something your mother told me about you. Did you?"

Her arrow was so unerring I answered honestly. "Yes."

"It was then you decided to call someone."

I nodded.

"And you wound up calling my stand-in."

"I was going to, but I didn't," I said. "In a million years I'd never have brought her here. I went out and she was here when I got back."

"How did she know it was safe?"

I had to smile. "Dorothy had called prior to that, only to discover I had a mistress. When she read the mistress had gone to San Francisco, she knew."

Rita giggled. "I was close."

"Very close," I admitted. "But if you could figure all that out, why'd you let it disturb you?"

"I didn't figure it all out," she said. "It simply came clear to me while I was doing the dance."

As late as it was, I'd never had a better reason for celebrating. I was already beginning to envision a future that exceeded my dreams. So I went out to the kitchen for a cold bottle of champagne, then I got some caviar. Only when I returned to the living room, she was out like a light. Even the champagne cork popping didn't raise her.

So I picked her up, and I realized I had never picked her up before. I couldn't get over how light she felt. It was hard to believe that anyone so fragile could have survived so much.

The following night, I got Mike to produce another of his candlelight extravaganzas. Since she was returning to San Francisco the next morning to finish *Pal Joey*, she assumed that was the occasion.

I told her that was reason enough, but it paled beside what we really had to celebrate. I told her she had a future even she couldn't imagine. Then I summoned up images of her dancing the previous night. Simply recalling it had me experiencing that excitement of discovery all over again.

I knew she'd be embarrassed—she always was when I got to bragging about her—but this time she seemed subdued. Especially when I got into the uniqueness of her comedic talent; no one with her beauty, I told her, had ever been so gifted.

The old Coquilles St. Jacques had come and gone, as well as the rest of the dinner, and I wasn't aware of having eaten. I could only think in terms of her freedom after she finished *Pal Joey*—freedom to be selective in her choice of roles, freedom to change her Love Goddess image. In the meantime, I said, if we couldn't find the right comic role, we would develop a script of our own to star her.

I got so carried away, I was oblivious of her silence. When moments passed and she still didn't say anything, I became concerned.

"Are you all right?"

"Yes."

"You haven't said a word. What are you thinking?"

"I was thinking about Pebble Beach," she said quietly. "And about your writing and my painting."

That was about the last thing I expected. "I figured we would do Pebble Beach as soon as you finished *Pal Joey*, I said. "But even before we do that, I'd like to put the whole routine you did last night on film."

Suddenly she looked very sad. "Why?" she said.

So I told her what it would mean to be able to show it to the studio heads to raise money for our own producing company—hers and mine. After all the talking I'd done, I guess she still didn't realize what a transformation of her image this would bring.

She just kept looking at me in that sad way of hers. So I thought of one last reason. "If we don't get it on film, I'm afraid we'll forget it."

She sort of turned away as though she couldn't bring herself to tell me what she was about to tell me. "I can't remember any of the things you say I did last night," she said.

"You *must* remember something."

"No," she said.

"Nothing at all?"

"The last thing I remember was making the Irish tea."

For the moment, I just sat there stunned. There were nights where I'd drunk too much and drawn a blank, but she had been so letter-perfect in her timing, her gestures—everything. The only time I had even seen her weave was at the very end of the evening.

It was like nothing I had ever run up against. I mean, you've been given Einstein's theory, but he can't remember having worked it out, or ever having shared it with you. And you forgot to write it down.

So I tried to explain to her what she had done. But it was like me trying to tell you what made W. C. Fields so funny if you'd never seen him. Desperation forced me to my feet, and I launched into those funny dance steps she did. But I could tell that was only making me look ridiculous. At least she didn't laugh. In fact, I could see I was only making her sadder.

"You really can't remember, can you?" I said, but it came out kind of weak, mostly because of that forlorn look on her face.

"Not after the first cup of Irish tea," she said.

"Do you remember how you made the Irish tea?"

Well, the whole room lit up, because she smiled.

So that was how I said we'd leave it. The very first thing after the wrap of *Pal Joey*, we'd stage a repeat of last night starting with the Irish tea. I'd even invite the cops if she thought that would help her remember, and if she felt she had to go back beyond that, I'd have the windows back in so she could knock them all out, too.

She was really smiling now; I think she liked the idea of having the windows to knock out again.

"But there's one thing I'd like even more," she said. "I'd like to go to Pebble Beach first."

We went to Pebble Beach. I wasn't aware of it then, but I was already beginning to trade off. I'd do whatever she wanted to do, in exchange for what I wanted. My obsession had begun—the notion of seeing her evolve into the screen's most beautiful comedienne. And since I was doing it for her benefit—or at least so I told myself—I wanted to keep everything harmonious.

While she may have been very slight and feminine, underneath it all she was used to getting her own way. She wasn't nearly the pushover I had at first thought. The people who were able to take advantage of her, I'd discovered, were those she didn't care about. But if it was a matter of someone or something important to her, then look out.

It was the first time I had ever taken a vacation in my life. Among all the things I learned from her, that was probably the first. I just couldn't believe our company could get a script in shape without me. So when she told me the world would keep spinning, even if I got off, I didn't believe her. But she was absolutely right.

Almost before I knew it, we were turning off the spectacular coast highway for Pebble Beach. And that's when it hit me. This would be the first time we would be out in public.

We were met by the manager, who led us down a narrow, winding road from the clubhouse, where the trees seemed to reach right up into the clouds. Once in a while I could see the ocean through them. It was as though we had left civilization behind us, it was that peaceful and quiet, that magical. Then we finally pulled up at a bungalow, overlooking the eighteenth green. And on the other side of the green was a great cliff, and beyond that, the ocean.

The surf came crashing up above the cliff, sending a spray of foam in every direction. I couldn't help noticing how she was enchanted by all of this, too, which only added to my growing concern.

The sound of that surf seemed just as loud when we had moved inside the bungalow. It was bigger than my apartment, and there was a roaring fire going and flowers everywhere, plus a bar that I couldn't have stocked better if I had come up a week ahead of time.

I was hoping Rita might take the scarf off before she disappeared somewhere in the back, but then I told myself that it was probably better that the manager hadn't recognized her. No sooner had she gone, though, than he stepped over close to me. The confidential way he lowered his voice made me know for sure the jig was up.

"I know I shouldn't mention this," he said, "but my daughter's Number One idol is Miss Hayworth. I can't tell you *what* it would mean to me to bring home an autograph. I know it's a terrible imposition."

"No, no, not at all," I said. "Do you want it right now?"

He started bowing and backing out. "If you'd just drop it off at the desk at your convenience. My daughter's name is Karen."

"If ever I have a daughter, that's what I'm going to call her," I said. "That's a beautiful name."

"I can't thank you enough," he said.

Rita had been listening, because as soon as the manager was out the door, she popped into the room and gave me a hug.

I sort of gave her the old cool gaze, just to play along with her. "You *are* a princess, aren't you?"

It was the real red-carpet treatment. I'd seen it before, but never as flamboyantly as I was to see it with Rita. They even knew the *car* when we drove up, as if they had spent their day awaiting the arrival of Miss Hayworth. And those jacketed deputies, who had everything out of the car and inside, in no more than a flash. And everything in the right place, too. And just as quickly, they were gone.

When we walked into the bedroom, there was a maid hanging up her clothes. I hadn't seen the maid come in, but I could tell Rita took it for granted she'd be there. At least she didn't seem a bit surprised.

She insisted, though, on personally unpacking the bag that contained her painting equipment, and all the paraphernalia for my writing. She even laid out these freshly sharpened pencils for me. You'd have thought I was going to knock off another *War and Peace* that night.

And then to show how she figured the rest of our time should go, she set up a gadget we practiced putting into. The gadget shot the ball back out if you did it right.

While she was doing all that, I threw my stuff into a couple of drawers. Then I set out on the table some scripts and novels that I had brought to read. And one book I placed in a strategically prominent position. It was a novel with a strong female lead in it called *They Came to Cordura*.

That evening, when we entered the dining room, it was just like that time in Paris when she walked across the lobby of the Ritz. There was a sudden buzz of conversation, then we started to move with the maitre d', and like a flattening wave, a hush followed.

If I hadn't come to know her as I had, I would have thought her wonderfully impervious to all eyes. But I knew that wasn't Rita. I could sense her personality changing from the moment we walked in and the maitre d' began fawning over her. Unlike any other performer I ever met, Rita was made really uncomfortable by such obsequiousness, and would immediately start to withdraw into herself. So it was a very subdued dinner, until I discovered the person at the next table was Tony Lema, one of the very best of the nation's professional golfers. It was easy to see he was dying to meet Rita Hayworth, and in no time at all we were talking courses and the proper clubs for tricky patches. Even Rita ventured a small distance out of her shell, so when we left, I invited Tony over the next evening for drinks.

We went to bed early because of our dawn tee-off time, so when I woke up in the middle of the night, I was startled to find Rita sitting up reading. When I asked her what woke her up, she hesitated, then admitted it was my having asked Tony over for drinks. She'd got to wondering—since it would be our last evening there—if we had to do that. Had I forgotten the painting and the writing we had planned for that time?

She had me there. So I tried subtly to change the subject. I picked up *They Came to Cordura,* and sort of thumbed through it.

"I thought you might enjoy this," I said. "There's just one female character with all these men, and I found her very complex, very interesting."

"Yes," she said, peering at me over the half-glasses she used for reading, "but I found one I liked better."

"What's that?" I said.

"*Separate Tables.*"

I had counted on her liking *They Came to Cordura.* I knew Gary Cooper had already been signed to star in it, so it was an ideal opportunity for her to play opposite him.

"How'd you happen to start reading in the first place?" I said.

"I thought it might put me back to sleep," she said, "and I almost made it with *They Came to Cordura.*" She gave me a Cheshire-cat smile and started reading again.

Now it happened that *Separate Tables* was a hit play that our company planned as our next picture. It was already cast and had a starting date. And, in fact, I suddenly realized there was a part in it that encompassed everything I had hoped to find for Rita. But it was folly even to entertain such a thought at this late date, so I decided I'd better dismiss *Separate Tables* from her mind, then maybe I could get her to thinking again about *They Came to Cordura.*

"I'm surprised *Separate Tables* didn't put you to sleep," I said. "It did for Harold—and not once, but twice."

Well, she lowered the book, and peered at me over those half-moon glasses again. I have to admit, I really liked those half-moons on her because they gave her a sexy executive look.

So I told her how *Separate Tables* had been playing in London, and how Harold and I went to the theater to see it with a writer named

Bill Rose. The leading roles were played by Margaret Leighton and Eric Portman. The reason I didn't enjoy it more, I explained, was because of Harold's falling noisily asleep—at one point he was snoring so audibly someone in the stalls turned and shushed us.

In the intermission, while we were having a drink at the bar, old Harold started shaking his head. "It's the damnedest thing," he said, "but I paid $350,000 for that play, and I've seen it twice and I've fallen asleep both times."

Naturally, I expected a chuckle, but Rita never so much as smiled. "Is Margaret Leighton playing the part in your movie?"

"It's not my movie, it's Harold's movie."

"Is she playing the part?"

"No."

"She's such a wonderful actress."

"Yes, she is."

"Have you cast the part?"

I knew that's what she was coming to, so I don't know why I was stalling so, but I was. "Yes," I said. "Harold's got Vivien Leigh."

Ever so slowly she closed *Separate Tables* and put it on the night table, then she folded her glasses and put them back in their case. "Did you leave an early call?" she said.

I nodded. "I really haven't had anything to do with it," I said. "It's Harold's picture."

"I understand," she said, and I could tell she truly did, but for some reason that didn't make me feel any better. So I was still looking for something to say, when she added, "Shall I turn out the light?"

I guess I nodded, because all I remember was looking into those wonderfully sad eyes of hers, and trying to find that something to say. But with Vivien Leigh set for the one part, and her husband, Laurence Olivier, set to play opposite her and also direct, and with the whole project being Harold's, what more *was* there to say? So she turned out the light. I had no reason to feel that terrible, but I did.

There's no doubt about it, Pebble Beach has to be as beautiful a place to walk around as you'll ever find. And if you really want to get to know every nook and cranny, then you should play golf the way I did, where you're always looking for your golf ball.

It's a funny game, because if you're any kind of an athlete, it couldn't look easier. Although I had never owned a set of clubs, I'd hit balls on a driving range and it hadn't been all that difficult. So I fully expected to have Rita ohing and ahing all over the place at my performance. But except for teeing off on each hole, we practically never saw each other again, since I was all the time in the woods, or the side of a cliff, or buried in a bunker, or someplace even worse.

It wasn't helping the old ego any, either, the way Rita hit every ball right down the fairway, while our caddies did a lot of ohing and ahing. She didn't hit it far, but she brought that same beautiful rhythm to her swing that she brought to everything she did, whether it was walking or dancing or just giving a hug.

Only after all the ohing and ahing, dread ominousness would set in when I took a swipe at the ball. Then we'd hear it ricocheting around in the trees, which meant I'd be parting from Rita to do some more searching.

It was way back at the fourth or fifth hole that I practically quit talking to my caddy. I was in the woods, as usual, but just to make conversation after I had found my ball and hit it back on the fairway, I'd said, "These are really beautiful fairways here at Pebble Beach."

"Yes," he said, "very few people use them."

Anyway, we'd gotten to this hole—it was the fourteenth or fifteenth but it seemed more like the ninety-eighth or ninety-ninth—when we paused to let another twosome play through. Now one of them was a fat kid, and both of our caddies regarded him with awe. They said he might win the U.S. amateur championship and his name was Jack Nicklaus. Well, I can only tell you, on this particular hole that was over the ocean, not only did he hit the ball a country mile, but he hit it straight as an arrow.

It's curious how easy it is to recognize greatness in someone, even if you're not an expert at their trade. All I could think about, as I watched that fat kid move off, was, *What if no one had ever put a golf club in his hand?* Obviously, my mind wasn't on golf. In effect, I was saying to myself, as tragic as that would have been for Jack Nicklaus —and for the game of golf—it would be a tragedy of equal magnitude if no one gave Rita Hayworth the chance to play comedy.

While my mind had been wandering, Rita had hit her drive as straight as usual, but since it took a good 175 yards to carry the water, there was no way she could hit it far enough to get it across. So it had plunked into the ocean.

That's when I discovered we had only two balls left. So I told her we'd better not risk hitting any more on this hole.

"I never heard of playing a round of golf where you didn't play out each hole," she said, regarding me like an extraterrestrial. "Next time, I'll bring my own balls."

"I thought two dozen would be enough," I said.

"That one I hit into the water was the first *I've* lost," she said.

"Okay," I said. "But we've still only got one apiece left."

She looked at me again, carefully. "You mean you've lost twenty-one balls?"

That did make me feel a little sheepish. Of course, if I had lost that many, it was no wonder I'd done so much walking and seen so much of the splendid course.

Rita shrugged and teed up one of the two remaining balls. I don't think I ever rooted harder for a little old ball to make it. And once again her swing was perfection, but her drive fell just short and the ball plunked into the ocean.

The silence that followed was badly strained—even the caddies were glaring at me. So I offered her the last ball, but she just gave me that significant look.

"Go ahead," I said. "If you lose it, what difference, we've still got each other."

When she didn't pause at the next tee, I knew we were heading for the car and that the golf was over. It was all I could do not to blame that fat kid for having made my mind wander, when it hit me: It wasn't the golf balls at all. When something was truly important to Rita, she never could bring herself to let you know it. And what was important was the painting and the writing, which we'd planned for that afternoon. And what with my losing all those balls, it had taken us twice as long to get through the golf as it would have ordinarily.

So even though it was as late as it was, I made sure I didn't waste a second once we got back to the bungalow. I knew she would take a shower, so I pretended I was going to take one, too. By the time Rita came out looking as fresh as only she could, I had everything in the car, including the painting and writing paraphernalia, and, of course, all that wine and cheese and caviar that helped make those French Impressionists so good.

I headed the car for an old square on a certain bluff I'd heard of, where Eugene O'Neill and Robert Louis Stevenson and a lot of others used to come to write. It was also a favorite view for generations of painters.

Luckily, it was deserted, except for the wind and the sound of the surf below. The trees around it were gnarled, wind-blasted, and you could see the old broken benches where the band used to play on Sundays. There was a rusted oil drum in the middle of the square that still had a lot of wood in it, so I got a fire going, then set the stuff in the basket out on one of the initial-scarred picnic tables.

In the meantime, she got out all the writing and painting gear, but when she turned and saw the spread I'd laid out, she didn't react at all. If ever I had counted on something to break the thaw, it was the caviar, but she didn't even sample it.

There was that faraway look creeping into her eyes again. So when she put the paper on the table in front of me with a handful of freshly sharpened pencils, I just sat there beside that swell lunch and suddenly wasn't hungry.

All I could do was stare at the blank sheet of paper and think about that distant expression, which I hadn't seen for such a long, long time. Dispelling that look was the first thing I was going to do. I had promised myself I would find the key and see to it she never had to feel that lost again. Well, you can imagine how hypocritical I felt, because since "the days of the cave" I hadn't really given it more than the occasional passing thought.

The sun was gone then, and the only light came from the flames flickering in the oil drum, and I was still staring at that blank sheet of paper.

"I hope you're thinking," she said, her voice so cold I flinched. I realized it was her way of prodding me, because it meant that much to her for us both to be good at what we were doing right then. I guess what I didn't realize was how it truly symbolized a kind of freedom to her.

I glanced out of the corner of my eye and saw how intent she was on sketching everything around her, so I decided to put something on that blank sheet of paper, no matter what.

Oddly enough, the only thing that came to mind was a poem I had written to a girl in college, when I thought I had lost her—that same heiress Dorothy had told me about on the visit that had proved fatal to so many windows. It also involved a square, like this one.

The Trees in the Square

It is never so cold
as alone in the square
so I hug the rough bark
and pretend not to care.
For some men love women
but those men are rare
who have nothing to love
but the trees in the square.

Why should I have thought of her right then I don't know, unless I was musing about how different my life might have been if I'd married her. Anyway, I became aware of Rita standing behind me. She had gotten so good at reading my mind that I had a bad moment, certain she was doing it again. At least there were no windows out where we were. I couldn't have been more wrong.

"After that terrible experience with the golf balls, I didn't think you could ever make it up to me," she said. "But you have."

"It's no good, not really," I said. I now felt more hypocritical than ever, since I could see she thought I'd written the poem for her.

She picked up the page and held it off from her, since she didn't have her glasses on, and she sort of studied it. Then she almost smiled. "If I think it's good, then *you* have to think it's good."

It was touching the way she could get to you; her sincerity was compelling. She had an innocence in her eyes that made her look all of thirteen. And then, like those other times, her eyes began to mist, and while she was still looking at the page, I could tell she wasn't seeing the poem any longer.

If only I'd had a more tangible clue to her wanderings, but this time I felt she was reaching out, like you sometimes do when you can't fall asleep at night, and you begin to fantasize about a magical place where you've never been before. Suddenly I crumpled that banal poem and threw it into the fire.

"I'd die if I couldn't do better by you than that. So let me tell you how I'm really going to make it up to you," I said. "I'm going to get you that part in *Separate Tables*."

She just stood there staring at me. In my whole life, I had never made such an impossible boast. But I wasn't thinking about Vivien Leigh's already being set, or that the project was totally out of my hands, or anything that so much as smacked of commonsense. I was carried away by the thought that Rita would do it.

I mean, I needed a slug or two of the old grape just to sober up, I was suddenly that drunk. So I opened the wine and caviar, and we dug into the French bread and the cheese. After the first bottle, which I virtually polished off myself, I told her she was getting to look more and more like Renoir the more she painted, which was a dread lie, of course, since he had a beard.

She smiled at the notion of herself with a beard. "So *that's* what's holding me back," she said.

In the days that followed, I grew increasingly jumpy. I wasn't making any headway on figuring how to get Rita the part in *Separate Tables*.

To break the tension, I decided we could use another restorative Pebble Beach weekend. I decided on the plane that I was going to tell Rita the whole truth about *Separate Tables*—let the chips fall where they may. On the flight back. It wasn't that I was putting it off, I told myself, just that I didn't want to raise a cloud over our stay.

We were there for three days. I don't think a minute of that time went by when I wasn't weighing possible alternatives. At Rita's insistence we hadn't brought the golf clubs, so that all our time could be devoted to painting and writing.

One thing to be said for writing. When you're in the mood I was in, you can sit with a blank piece of paper and, so long as you've got a sharpened pencil in hand, you can be thinking about anything. Rita had extracted a promise to show her what I'd written, then she would show me what she'd sketched. That was why with each passing day, I was getting more desperate. I figured with an alternative, I'd never have to get down to the serious business of writing.

It was the third day, the day we were to leave. I still had that same blank sheet of paper in front of me, while she was outside sketching, when the phone rang. Funny, it didn't have the sound of a miracle to it.

Ted was the only one who knew where we were, so I knew something was up. He told me the money people at United Artists had decided they needed a star of Burt Lancaster's caliber if they were going ahead with the financing of Separate Tables. That meant Burt would have to replace Olivier. If he wasn't to play the lead, Olivier had decided he would not continue as director. So Vivien Leigh had also decided to leave the picture.

"The part's Rita's, if she wants it," Ted said. "Harold's on the phone to her agent right now."

After I hung up, I stood watching Rita paint a moment before I told her. Her face lit up, but not the incandescence I'd expected.

"You said I'd get it, didn't you?"

I know I should have told her right then I had nothing to do with her being given the part. But I was high on the feeling you get when you say you can pull off a miracle, then do just that. Especially when you really care about someone, and they've got the kind of eyes she had, and she's looking at you like you were some kind of a god.

Of course, that old devil hindsight tells me that wasn't the real reason. I didn't tell her because I wanted her to feel beholden to me. My vision of her as the screen's most beautiful comedienne hadn't become the obsession it would become. But I already recognized how important it was that she feel some kind of obligation to me, if I was going to bring it off.

If I had to pick the single thing Rita liked best about Terence Rattigan, it was his golf game. You'd have thought it would have been his enthusiasm for her playing in Separate Tables, because he was nearly as delighted as I was at the outcome. But he really shone on the links with those nifty manners that are so peculiarly English and his gift for entertaining gossip.

He was staying with Kay Kendall and Rex Harrison, and he'd invariably give us a rundown on the highlights of their marriage. Clearly Terry was giving Rita a lot of new ideas, because when Kay Kendall got put out with Rex, she didn't stop at breaking windows. So I have to admit I didn't enjoy these accounts as much as Rita did.

Unfortunately, when Olivier got ready to leave town, Terry decided he should go back at the same time. I was disappointed, because the problems with the script had in no way been solved, and I'd been looking forward to working with Terry. But he explained that he'd been too close to the writing for too long to be of any further use. I never thought to question it, but Rita told me later his departure had been motivated by an old loyalty to Olivier.

It was a melancholy round of golf, our last round, and after Rita and I had said goodbye to Rattigan over drinks at our place, we got to reminiscing about the fine times we'd had. Like that cold, blustery day when Harold took a group of high-powered guests out on the *Pursuit*. Everyone was shivering and feeling thoroughly miserable, but no one was admitting it, until someone asked old Terry if he enjoyed yachting.

"Yes, if you're referring to hors d'oeuvres on the *Queen Elizabeth* at cocktail time," he said, all six feet of him looking quintessentially elegant in his double-breasted blazer and ascot. "When she's lying at anchor, of course."

"Terence has known suffering and pain," Rita said, and where I had been laughing, I saw she was serious and had a sadness in her eyes. "That's why he's such a fine writer." Her manner became very confidential as it always did when she was deeply touched, and her voice dropped to a near whisper. In Terry's case, she confided, it was his longtime obsession with a dwarf.

"You mean Terence Rattigan is in love with a *dwarf?*" I said. "I just can't believe he'd walk so tall, if he really cared that deeply about someone so small."

"Not so loud," Rita cautioned, even though we were alone in our apartment. "I know he wouldn't want us talking about such a personal thing."

By now I knew we were playing our old game. Rita was gently reminding me of something she knew I needed badly to know: You had to know pain and suffering if you ever expected to be a serious artist.

"I guess they can be real attractive, those dwarfs," I said. "Did he say whether she had a good figure, or anything like that?"

Her eyes got even darker. "It isn't a she. It's a he."

"He's in love with a male dwarf!" I exclaimed.

"Not so loud!"

Of all the scripts I've worked on for our company, *Separate Tables* was a unique experience—the first time I'd started with a proven success. And the first time I'd been given such an outstanding cast as Burt Lancaster, Rita Hayworth, Deborah Kerr, and David Niven.

Although I had expected problems, since the two plays that made up the original stage production had to be integrated into one, they seemed to fall naturally into place. I had two fine writers to work with, since we had the pressure of time. But when the job was finished inside of three weeks, we'd done it with time to spare. It made us wonder, considering the months Olivier had put in on the project —and that with the benefit of Rattigan, the original author. I got so excited I called Carol Reed in London in the hope he might want to direct, but he said he had other commitments. So in the end, my biggest reward came from Rita, who I could see was more than pleased.

One of the things you can't escape in making a picture is the eternal on-the-set gossip. Nothing is sacred, nothing is secret however tight the security. So it was with Rita during the rehearsal period. I don't know how many times I heard she would have to be replaced, because she spoke so softly she was nearly inaudible.

I wasn't about to go near those rehearsals, no matter what, but I did breathe a sigh of relief when the first day of shooting rolled around without incident.

It was fun being back in our old routine. Mike and I dropped Rita off at the studio every morning, then I went on to the office. We even got back to referring to her as the Princess.

The company must have been a couple of weeks into the shooting when Burt asked me to take a look at the rushes with him. I have to admit I was nervous. If something was cockeyed, it's a cinch I wasn't going to say anything to Rita about it. So we looked at the rushes and something was cockeyed, all right.

Everything seemed somehow flat. Rita couldn't have looked lovelier in what film there was on her, and her dialogue came through beautifully, so all that was a relief. But something was still cockeyed. It hit us both at about the same time. In the theater, when Eric Portman had played the Major, he had employed an infinitely effective piece of business. He'd affected a slight limp, with his open palm held across his chest, so that he evoked immediate audience response. I know I had a lump in my throat just watching his entrance—and that, before he ever said a word. David Niven's approach to the film was to do without that business. We learned later that he hadn't wanted to be accused of merely imitating Portman, determined as he was to bring his own interpretation to the role. Only his own interpretation just didn't come off. And since the one person you had to empathize with was the Major, it was no wonder everything had fallen flat.

Fortunately, David Niven is the professional's professional. Once he was told how vital that small piece of business was, he readily agreed to restore it. That necessitated reshooting all his scenes, but it was well worth it—especially for Niven, who wound up winning an Oscar.

After they had done the reshooting, Burt and I looked at the rushes again. It was amazing what a difference Niven's transformation made to everybody's performance. I can't tell you how pleased I was with Rita's work. If ever there was a reason for getting the cave in shape for a celebratory weekend, this was it.

Now it not only happened to be a Friday, but it was also a hot day outside, so it was perfect for dropping the temperature to near-freezing in the cave. Once I'd adjusted all the thermostats and had the fires going in the fireplaces, I sprung my first surprise. I'd borrowed a big

old St. Bernard from a friend, and when I rang the bell, Mike let the
dog out of the kitchen.

You should have seen Rita's face light up when he came to her with
a cask of brandy around his neck, spigot and all. Since I'd already set
out the glasses, we had ourselves a few snifters. Rita was in such a
nifty mood, I could hardly keep from telling her how great I thought
she'd been in the rushes. But since by now I knew how she withdrew
at just about any kind of flattery, I used the oblique approach instead.
I told her a story Joe DiMaggio had once told me. Ted Williams was
due to get his 350th home run or 3,000th hit or something, so after
the Yankee game that night Joe had traveled from New York up to
Boston. He had timed it perfectly, because Williams broke the record. Only Joe didn't go back after the game to congratulate him.

"Imagine," I told her, "here were the two greatest baseball players
of the day, and one takes the night off to see the other set a record,
then doesn't even let him know he was in the stands.

"Think what it would have meant to Ted," I said, "to have had Joe
compliment him in person. Instead, he never even knew he was
there."

Well, she looked up from hugging that big old St. Bernard, who
was getting so much affection I began to wonder if I'd been all that
bright in borrowing him in the first place.

"I don't know," she said thoughtfully. "Maybe it was better that
way."

"Better!" I exclaimed. "It was really dumb. As a performer you
should know precisely how much it means to have your work appreciated by someone else."

Even though I tried to keep the irritation out of my voice, she
must have felt it, because she quit hugging the St. Bernard for a
moment.

"The more I think about it," she said, "the more I think Joe Di-
Maggio handled it perfectly."

But she must have felt my terrible sense of rejection, because the
next thing I knew she had the castanets going, that fabulous black,
wide-brimmed gaucho hat on, and she had launched into brilliant
variations on those comedy routines she'd created on the night of our
romantic misunderstanding. I just sat back, sipping the brandy and

once in a while changing a cassette, all the while plotting the best way to get those routines on film without her knowing it. A hidden camera was the obvious solution. Because I knew now that I had to build a film for her around that dancing character she had created—*had* to direct her in it.

My experience as a director was at that point limited—one film, *The Kentuckian*, and that with a lot of help from Burt. I hate to admit it, but I was a basket case the first day on the set. Since Burt was going to star, as well as direct the film, he needed someone to supervise the shooting when he was in a scene. I'd worked on the development of the script, so it was only natural he should figure I knew *something* about it. But it also meant I had to shout "action," and "cut," and determine whether a scene was ready for a print—all that high-powered directorial rigamarole.

Anyway, Burt rehearsed everybody that first day, and when they were letter-perfect, I took over. Naturally, I had beginner's nerves, so I'd say "action" and everyone would start emoting all over the place, then I'd hear a voice say "speed." Well, you're not supposed to say "action" until you hear that voice say "speed," because the effect on film is that everybody looks as if they're walking in molasses.

I must have screwed things up about four times straight before Burt took me aside. He had infinite patience, because even then all he said was, "Everybody's beginning to think we're a couple of okies, so can't you just wait until you hear 'speed' before you say 'action'?"

So you can see I wasn't without *some* preparation for directing—about as much as any of the directors I've worked with, with the exception, that is, of Carol Reed. In my theory of successful filmmaking, all that counts—beyond a fine script and good actors—is the morale of the people. Especially the leading lady. That's why I felt so confident in my dreams of directorial glory, since who would be better than me when the leading lady was Rita Hayworth?

There was one other important factor, and that was her drinking. My experience on the night of the broken windows had taught me it was important she have a little, but not too much—enough so she'd get into her dance routines, but not so much that she'd forget she had done them the next day.

*   *   *

In the days that followed, I noticed an invitation to the preview of *Pal Joey* lying neglected on the hall table. It was puzzling to me that Rita could invest all that energy and time in making a picture and then not be the least bit curious about the outcome. So when she began to grow increasingly withdrawn as the date of the premiere drew near, I figured it must be getting to her after all.

But the premiere came and went, and her melancholy persisted, so I knew it had nothing to do with *Pal Joey*. Then one morning Mike said she told him she wasn't going to ride in with us. I'd seen the shooting schedule and knew she was supposed to be working that day. I'd never known her to miss a day's shooting before, so I sensed something must have gone seriously awry. After a deal of wary circling around the subject, I got her to confess that she didn't like the way things were going on the set, so she'd decided not to return to the picture.

Her principal grievance was with my partner, Harold Hecht, who she kept referring to as "the producer." She couldn't bear having "the producer" watching her every move from behind the camera "with his beady little eyes," then going on and on to the director in endless, whispered conversation.

It's odd how you never really look at a fellow—even after all the years I'd spent with Harold—until someone says something telling about him. Suddenly, instead of my partner, he was the enemy with beady eyes. To keep Rita on the picture I had to convince her Harold was a genial genius—not the easiest of challenges, if you happened to know him.

Although once I got talking about him, and explaining how very human his problems were—the loneliness of the creative spirit—she listened up. Poor old Harold had no one to turn to, I told her, but the man who made his shirts on Rodeo Drive. He was known as Yvel, the shirtmaker, which was Levy spelled backwards. In the lonely evenings Harold had to commission yet another shirt, just so he'd have someone to talk to about his scripts and other creative enterprises. But the day came when Yvel retired with all the money he had made from making those shirts and became plain Levy again. And once he did, he lost his interest in matters creative and moved from Rodeo Drive to Palm Springs. So poor old Harold was once again without a confidant—until he discovered his *directors* had nothing but time on their hands once the camera started rolling, which was why he was always talking to them on the set.

Instead of beginning to smile and feel a certain sympathy for "the producer," Rita looked somber. "You make him sound like a joke."

"Yes," I agreed.

"Does he know he's a joke?"

"If he doesn't, then he's not laughing at himself."

"What does that mean?"

"I've found there are only two paths in our business," I said. "Either you laugh at yourself, or you drink."

Well, for the first time I seemed to have struck a chord, because her eyes widened. "That's what I said to myself today," she said. "Our producer is a drinker."

"If he is, then that's sad."

"You mean it would be better if he was laughing at himself?"

"Yes."

She had been studying me carefully through all this. Now she narrowed her eyes. "Are *you* a joke?"

Well, for the first time I had to smile. "Of course I am," I said. "I've been laughing at myself ever since I realized somebody upstairs put us here so He could enjoy Himself."

I couldn't tell whether she was buying any of this, but at least she wasn't looking all that grim anymore. "Does Burt know he's a joke?"

"Only half a joke," I corrected her. "He thinks he has an image, so he's only half laughing at himself." Then, knowing how she liked Burt, I quickly added, "But that's good, because he's only wasting half his time being serious."

She seemed to mull that over, then smiled. "I guess I should really feel sorry for our producer."

"You see, you are amused," I said. I was sure I had won the day. "So no matter how you look at it, whether it's me or Harold, or finishing *Separate Tables* with him behind the camera, it's all a joke."

"Not quite," she said, and the smile vanished. "It's only a joke when the producer stops taking himself seriously. So when he stops whispering behind the camera, I'll get back to the set and start enjoying the joke."

Everything in our future depended on her finishing *Separate Tables*. It was the first big step toward changing her image, which meant the first big step for me and my dream of directing her.

"I was willing to break every rule of decency to get you into *Separate Tables*." I was coldly furious. "I figured after all these years of playing parts you hated—parts that capitalized on an image you loathed—you would do anything, suffer anything to change. You stand here, ready to turn your back on your one chance to become a new person with a new image. Your one chance to *be* more than the Love Goddess. Your one chance to *do* more than just grow old!"

In all the years I had known her, the only other time I saw her turn that pale was during the Christmas Eve encounter with Harry Cohn. It was all she could do to keep her voice steady.

"I told you what it would take for me to go back on that picture," she said. Then, in a near whisper, she added, "I'm sorry."

In looking back, I can see the episode was an excuse for her to break away from the business entirely. There was no other reason for her to have so inflated a minor incident. I must have sensed it at the time, which was why I went to such lengths to put it behind us.

Anyway, the way she said those two words, "I'm sorry," made me suddenly feel I would do anything to protect her. She looked that young, frightened, alone, and defenseless.

"If you're not going to finish *Separate Tables*, you're going to have time on your hands," I said. "Maybe we should use some of it to get married."

She just stood there staring at me. I have never seen anyone so still. I'd expected a laugh, or maybe a joke, since the thought of marriage was hardly unfamiliar to her. But instead, what seemed like forever went by. Then her eyes misted with a different kind of tears than any I'd seen there before. And then she was hugging me.

Naturally, when you get breathing that kind of rarefied air, your next thoughts are champagne and a little celebrating. Only right away, Rita became Miss Hayworth, a guise she hadn't assumed for quite some time.

"You're *certainly* not going to drink champagne before going to work," she said very sternly.

"I didn't think I'd *go* to work today, since you're not going in," I said. "It wouldn't be the same with just me and Mike in the car—not when we've grown used to riding with a princess."

"I never thought of that," she said. Then she got a wicked gleam in her eye. "Of course I'll ride in with you. And as long as I am, I might as well finish *Separate Tables*. Don't you think?"

PART FOUR

PART FOUR

ONCE we got the marriage license in Santa Monica, Rita's every move became front-page news. Since she had never married in the church, she mentioned the idea, but all the publicity made us decide the simpler we could keep things, the easier it would be to maintain our privacy.

We had rented a house, so we decided to have the wedding there. The only guests were members of our respective families, with a couple of exceptions. Naturally, we had Schiffer, who had helped get me into all this. And, of course, his anchor. Then there was Bernie Kamber. It was important for him to be there, because once the press discovered what had happened, Bernie would have the tricky job of explaining why they hadn't been invited.

Since Bernie was a public-relations man by trade, his reaction pretty well summed up everyone else's, outside of our families. I had finally given him something to write about—at last I would have an identity. If Bernie had been less the diplomat, he'd have said I would now be Mister Hayworth. The thought wasn't new to me, nor did it bother me, but I had to smile to myself at Bernie's acknowledging that I finally achieved true stature in the industry.

The wedding was a civil ceremony, over before the ice in your drink had a chance to melt. It was the first time I had met Rita's brother Vernon, who had come with his wife. He was several years younger, with the same good looks.

My mother provided the highlight of the afternoon by surrendering my baby album to Rita. She made a real ritual out of it. So between that, and all the champagne toasts, it was an afternoon full of laughter.

In departing, my folks each had a piece of marital advice. "Don't cut your hair, no matter what," my mother told Rita enigmatically.

Then my father took my hand with great seriousness. "If you want to succeed in the world, now you're married, when you wake up in the morning, get up."

I knew he had said it solely for Rita's benefit. She burst into laughter. He had come to enjoy making her laugh as much as I did. So we left for our honeymoon on that optimistic note.

Everyone had been curious about our honeymoon, but Rita had sworn me to secrecy. Since it was the last day of the apartment lease, she had decided we should spend the first night there. It was her way of saying goodbye to everything she'd come to love about the cave.

What I hadn't told Rita was that I'd had a camera hidden in the apartment while she had been working on the set of *Separate Tables*. It seemed like the perfect way to record this night for our old age. And if I got lucky, all those nifty dance routines, too. One thing I was certain of—no one would get a bigger kick out of it than she would when she saw the film.

Once I had the fires going and we were opening our first bottle of Dom Perignon, I asked her what my mother had meant when she warned her not to cut her hair?

Rita smiled to herself. "Your mother said when your father was courting her, he loved to drop by after she'd washed her hair and brush it for her."

"*My* father did that?"

I must have shown such shock that she frowned. "What's the matter with that?"

"Well," I hedged, "nothing, I guess."

"Then why did you make that face?" She shook her head. "I should have known better."

I was already saying to myself, if I could only learn from Rita, and shut up and listen. "It seems so intimate," I managed. "I mean, my own father."

"I'm not about to ask you to brush my hair," she said.

"I've always wanted to," I admitted. "But it's like stealing a whiff from one of your perfume atomizers. A person just doesn't admit those things."

"Your father didn't. Your mother was the one who told me."

"Of course."

When she saw how serious I'd become, she got to smiling again. "Your mother said her hair reached to her knees in those days."

The first thing I had ever noticed about Rita was her hair. But it had never struck me until then how much alike their hair was. Even to the glorious auburn color. But I didn't say any of that; I was finally smart enough just to listen.

"Your mother told me that a new hair style was sweeping the country. So the day before her wedding, she got it bobbed. But your father didn't notice it until they were alone together on the first night of their honeymoon."

"Oh boy!" I whistled. "I can see her taking off her wedding bonnet, while he's getting out the brush."

Rita sighed. "Now don't start to make fun of everything," she said gravely. "That was exactly what happened. Your mother said he was so furious with her, they never slept together that first night."

"That's an incredible story," I said. "And to think it involved my own parents! What did you say to my mother after she told you?" I asked.

"It wasn't what I said, it was what I was thinking," Rita replied, and I could see that dangerous gleam in her eye. "If I had only heard the story sooner, I would have gotten my head shaved."

The other revelation involved Rita. It was these two revelations that got our honeymoon off to such a nifty start. She had been musing about a date for our next trip to paint and write.

"When did you know you really wanted to paint?" I asked her.

"I was sitting on a bench, sketching in the Bois de Boulogne in Paris—just doodling, really—when a man paused beside me. I didn't look up because I figured he would go away. But after a few moments, he suggested some things I should do with the pencil. His voice was rough, and when I looked up I saw his clothes were shabby. I started to get up to move away, when I realized I was looking into the face of Maurice Utrillo."

Rita sighed at the recollection. It reminded me of the young clerk, when we had gone for our license. He had sighed exactly like that—right down to his shoes—when he recognized her.

"Monsieur Utrillo said, 'Try it, just try it.' I was so overcome I could hardly wield the pencil, but I did, and just changing a line here and there made all the difference."

"He knew who you were."

"No. I was purposely bundled up so no one would recognize me," Rita said. "I had on a floppy hat, my coat collar turned up, all of that."

"He knew you knew who he was?"

"Of course. I said I didn't know why he should be interested in the way I drew. That made him chuckle. He said to be perfectly frank, what had interested him was the bone structure in my face."

She paused, smiling to herself, before she went on. " 'Will that help make me a better painter?' I asked him. He chuckled again. 'No,' he said, 'but it will make a painter interested in you, even when you're one hundred.' "

"Did he ask you to pose?"

"Yes."

"He knew."

"No. It was only after he asked where to call me—when I had to give him my name—that he knew."

"Did you meet him again?"

"Yes," she said, "but he didn't ask me to pose once he knew who I was. We met for tea in his studio in Montmartre. He had done a painting for me in the meantime."

"I'd love to see it."

"You will," she said. "It's in storage."

She went on to tell me of all they talked about that afternoon as the light of Montmartre faded into evening. She said he told her what went through his mind when he painted, and how he tried to use his figures, as well as the distant backgrounds. He told her the crucial thing was how much of himself an artist can bring to his work. She said in her whole life she had never been so enchanted. When she left him that day, he had opened a whole new world to her.

It was the most I had ever heard Rita reveal about her past. To

show how enthralled I was, I even forgot the reason for having set out the golf clubs, which had got her going that other time. Plus the tea and the Irish whiskey.

I had always said wine is for the victor. Only with Rita, her castanets took the place of the grape. When she felt triumphant, sooner or later she would have them going. So it wasn't long before they found their way to her slender fingers. She hadn't had so much as a sip of Irish tea, but her dancing was the best I'd ever seen. And then it hit me.

The camera!

Naturally, I turned it on. And along with activating it, I started unobtrusively downing most of her drinks as well as mine. I remember saying to myself that not only would I get it all on film, but by drinking her drinks I'd ensure that the next morning she'd remember everything that happened.

So by the time we got into the Irish tea—and I made sure to put only a small slug of Irish whiskey in hers—everything was going splendidly. I was even attempting a few dips and glides myself since it always gave her such a kick. But don't think that, in my own mind, I wasn't thinking of the Palace.

The next thing I remember clearly was waking up early the following morning to what seemed an unusual chill. I didn't have to check the thermostats, because in making a tour of the place I noticed that a number of the new living-room windows had vanished. Now while I didn't remember Rita's actually breaking them, I had to admit I didn't remember her swinging the golf club, either.

So while she was still asleep, I got the camera and hid it in the trunk of the car. Then I woke her and told her it was such a swell dawn that we ought to get an early start up the coast, as long as we had the painting and writing gear in the car. As soon as I mentioned painting and writing, she was ready to go.

We drove to a place we'd heard of outside Santa Barbara that had isolated bungalows, winding woodland trails, for wandering and painting, and meals you could take in your cottage. It couldn't have suited us better.

Some two days passed before I thought to call Ted, and I found him in a real dither. He had found us a dream house, and if we didn't come right back to town, we stood to lose it. Since I'd made a point with Ted about how the perfect house could make a marriage, there was nothing for it but to head back.

Ted had done it again. The house was beyond our wildest expectations. Perched on a hill up behind Sunset and the Beverly Hills Hotel, it was so artfully landscaped that it seemed all by itself, even though you could look out past the pool in the back and see the city in the distance below. And that was all you could see. Not a trace of another house, not a telephone pole, not so much as a television antenna. I had been raised to believe your home was truly your fortress, and Ted had certainly found ours.

Beyond that, Ted told us, if we could pay cash for the property, we could get one whale of a deal. Only Rita and I had a perpetual cash-flow problem. So the three of us sat and pondered the various routes to raising that kind of money.

Finally, it came down to two options—I could put myself in hock for the next couple of years, or Rita could do *They Came to Cordura*. In the end, she decided the most efficient way to get the house would be for her to do the picture. Since it was early spring, and shooting wasn't to begin until late fall, it all seemed a long way off.

In retrospect, I'd like to believe that—remembering her earlier reluctance about the project—I didn't put pressure on her, but I know better. They had signed Robert Rossen, who had done *The Hustler*, to write and direct *Cordura*. They had Gary Cooper to play opposite her. The novel had gotten good reviews. It had the potential to be a worthy successor to *Separate Tables*, another step in my reshaping of her career. So even if I could have arranged the loan, I admit I would have done it no differently.

There was the sense of opening the pages of a brand-new book when we moved into that house. I knew we were headed in the right direction from the moment Rita took charge of the decorating. Although she had hired a professional, he was relegated to rounding up swatches and carrying out her plans. She had the same inventiveness and flair that she brought to the clothes she wore and the canvases she painted. Even while the work was going on, everyone who entered the house was struck by its unique beauty.

Then there were her paintings. Their hanging provided the final touch. She gave the Utrillo pride of place above the living-room fireplace. The painting was of the Bois, and there was a bench, which could only have been the one she had been sitting on when Utrillo approached her. Instead of a spring day, everything was covered with snow. In fact, the entire oil was done in various shades of white. It was hauntingly beautiful, and it reflected the spirit of the man who had painted it. The more I looked at it, the more of him I found in it —that particular alchemy he had told Rita was the first obligation of the artist. We made a pact as we lifted the painting into place. We would look up Utrillo on our first visit to Paris.

Besides the Utrillo, she had several other paintings by well-known artists, but as she explained, she had picked them up when they were still striving for recognition. That was another of her remarkable qualities—the way she was never one to join the pack. The records she brought home were invariably by unknowns. But it was amazing how many became famous. She had an infallible instinct for talent.

If I had a complaint, it was because nothing of hers adorned the walls. So I took the liberty of placing several in the den and in our bedroom. But when I got home that night they had been replaced. Before I could comment, she headed me off.

"I've decided we'll hang my paintings the day you publish your first book," she said, smiling. I could see she was proud of her decision. "It wouldn't be fair otherwise."

Our final chore was arranging the wedding gifts and writing endless thank-you notes. Just when I thought we were finished, Rita frowned. "I've been thinking about that present from the producer," she said, meaning Harold Hecht. "I can't accept it, feeling the way I did about him."

Harold's gift had been the most lavish of all those we had received. It was a $5,000 credit at Adrian's, one of the reigning fashion designers.

"He doesn't know how you felt," I said, "unless you told him. You didn't, did you?"

"No, but I wanted to."

"Well, you didn't, and that's all that counts," I said. "If you turn down his gift now, he'll never understand why you don't like him."

"You mean I should have told him in the first place?"

"No," I said. "If you had, you wouldn't have a five-thousand-dollar credit at Adrian's."

"You know what Bernard Shaw said?"

"What?"

"The woes of marriage begin with the anarchistic scramble for money."

"He said that, but he didn't mention marriage."

"No, but he meant to," Rita said, looking grim, "because he was referring to you."

Three months later the place was ready for an unveiling. So when Rita said she would leave the guest list to me, I thought it would be the perfect opportunity to combine business with pleasure.

Since more then eight people represented a crowd to Rita, and she hated crowds, I invited eight of the most successful in the industry, each of whom could be helpful in the metamorphosis I envisioned for her. I picked a Sunday because I liked the idea of a brunch by the pool.

I had never felt so content as I did that day. Everyone was lethargic with Bloody Marys and steaks. I was contemplating how each of them would fit into our plans, when my eye came to Rita. If ever she should be at peace with the world, I thought, it should be at this very moment. She was staring out at the city below. There was that faraway, lost expression again. I moved over to her, but she wasn't aware of me, even when I took her hand. I never felt such cold fingers. So when she finally spoke, it came as a relief.

"Do you suppose it would be all right if we went for a drive?" she said, so softly I barely heard her. When I hesitated, not because of our guests, but because of my concern, she quickly added, "We'll only be gone for a few minutes."

By the time I was turning the car around in the drive, I could feel her begin to relax. My relief turned to anger. I had never known anyone who had the world so completely at their fingertips, yet she wasn't enjoying it. Not really. Otherwise, why did she wander off into another world, and where did she go when she got that lost look?

"Not so fast."

I probably should have stopped for the signal that had turned yellow at the corner, but instead, I raced through it.

"Please!" she said sharply. "Will you *please* drive more carefully!"

That triggered all the frustration I was feeling. In a burst of rage, I put the gas pedal to the floor. We were ducking and dodging cars at speed, until I pulled into a little park in Holmby Hills. Rita was shaking all over. If I had forgotten her terror of traffic, I might have had some excuse, but I hadn't. I'd wanted to punish her, and I had.

There was no way I could have felt smaller or more contemptible as I watched her clenching and unclenching those lovely, slender fingers, while staring down at them and saying, over and over again, "I'm sorry, I'm sorry."

And I kept saying, "It's all right, it's all right." I had my arm around her, and finally she calmed down enough so that I could lead her out of the car.

One of the real jewels in our part of town is this tiny park. I fell in love with it because it reminded me of St. James's Park in London. There's something comforting and British about the lawn bowling greens, and the pitch-and-putt golf course, and all those trees. And it's almost always deserted. So it's always been a haven for me.

Instinct must have brought me there, because once we started walking, I could see the tension leaving Rita. I knew that she would pause at each of the holes on the golf course, that she would love the ornamental bridge over the little stream. By the time we had cut through the picnic area, making one complete circuit, she had begun to be her old self.

"It's inexcusable that anything can be so lovely, with no one here to appreciate it," she said. "I don't know why you've kept it such a secret."

There is something deeply rewarding about sharing a discovery, but you know you've got a true convert when they start telling *you* all the virtues you already know it possesses. We had settled on a bench under some towering eucalyptuses that almost hid the second green. I felt such relief that I didn't mind just sitting and listening for once. She went on about the park for a spell, then fell silent.

"I *am* sorry," she said. "I really am."

I figured if I kept quiet long enough, she might come to what was bothering her. I had long ago found out that if I pried, she closed up tight. "No need to be," I said. "I just wish I knew where you went, when you go away. Maybe I could go with you."

She thought about that. "You could have once. I don't know about now."

"You mean I've changed?"

"I'm not sure."

She studied me. I waited. Then she took me all the way back to that first meeting at her house. She warned me I might not feel flattered at what she had to say, because she had found me immature, frivolous, and seriously unsure of myself. But it was those very qualities that had intrigued her. Now, while she still saw those same qualities occasionally on the surface, underneath she said, I had become quite sure of myself.

"I don't know what to say," I said, and I didn't.

She smiled gently, which meant she liked my answer. "I'll risk it."

She went way back—before my first seeing her in Tijuana—back to her twelfth birthday. She was opening in a dance act with her father on an amusement pier in New Jersey. It had been a long day's rehearsing. Her father had paused to go over the lighting with an electrician. She was so weary she slipped outside for a breather, and even the air tasted good. Then she heard the music of a carousel. The next thing, she was on one of the horses. It made her forget she still had two shows to do that night. Suddenly, she was in another world, celebrating her birthday. That was where her father found her.

"Ever since then, if I don't like where I am, or who I'm with, or myself—if I just don't like me, which happens the most often—then that carousel comes to mind, and once I hear the music, I am back on that horse." She paused and sighed. It was that sigh of hers that never failed to get me. "It always makes me sad. Because somehow, someone or something will be along, and then I'll have to leave."

That explained why her eyes misted when she got that look. It was the music of the carousel fading. Even I could figure that one out. I was still thinking of all she had said, when she got to her feet.

"Have I changed?"

She had started to move away, then turned back to me.

"You're a lot more positive about what you want from life," I said, "and I'm not talking about your picture career."

"Yes, I think I am."

We started walking. "Those people at the house," I said. "You didn't like my guest list?"

"Not particularly."

"They can be important to our future."

"I suppose."

"You told me to do the inviting."

"I'm not blaming you."

That told me something, so I paused, knowing she would. "You'd rather I'd invited our families."

"Your family," she corrected me.

"I didn't mean your father," I said. "I was thinking of your brother and his wife."

"Yes, we should have had them."

"Next time you handle the guest list."

She didn't answer, but started walking again, which told me it wasn't the people back at the house. That left only one other thing that could have caused her such anxiety—the house itself. It was the last thing I wanted to believe, because I loved everything *about* that house. Only the farther we walked, the surer I became, until finally I had to know.

"If it's the house," I blurted out, "we're not stuck with it, you know." She cocked her head, like a wary animal that pricks its ears. "You can blow it up, and everything with it. I'll even get the dynamite, if you'll just tell me what's behind your thinking."

Those great, innocent eyes of hers opened wide. For the first time, I felt we were back in the same ball club. I could see the glimmering of a great big smile in all those flecks of color.

"Let's go back and blow it up," she said, and she meant it.

I only mentioned the dynamite in the first place because I was working for a smile. She really shook me. "You don't like the house?" I finally managed.

I could tell by the way she paused, she was aware of her impact. "Of course I like the house."

"Then what is it?"

"I suddenly felt trapped."

So my hunch about *Cordura*, which meant committing her future to another picture, had been right. At least I knew something about her that I hadn't before. She was a gypsy at heart, and gypsies don't sign away their future. They live for today and carry their worldly goods with them. Which means they don't have houses, so they don't have to come home. Since they never grow up, they are without responsibilities. At least, that was my idea of a gypsy. But one thing I did know. I'd never met anyone I really cared about who didn't have a gypsy inside, trying to get out.

We were previewing *Separate Tables* the following week. To my amazement, Rita decided to attend. The picture got a nifty reception from the audience, and the reviewers were impressed with her performance. But it was Margaret Leighton's reaction that made the greatest impression on me.

"If I could have done the part in the theater as well as your wife did it on screen," Miss Leighton told me, "they'd never have had her take my place."

Since I happened to believe that Margaret Leighton was the world's greatest living actress, I couldn't wait to repeat her words to Rita. That was when I knew Rita knew she had done just fine. "They did kind of like me," she said in that soft, special way of hers, "didn't they?"

There had been no further mention of the house, nor had we invited anyone else over. I knew we hadn't put the problem to rest, but I had been so tied up working with a writer on the final draft of Bernard Shaw's *The Devil's Disciple*, our company's next picture, that I had no time for anything. I hadn't even been able to play golf, or go off writing and painting, or any of the other things that got Rita out of the house, and which she liked most to do.

I could tell my gypsy was getting deeply restless. We were saying a little less to each other, and drinking a little more at the end of each day. One night I woke up at two in the morning with a glow. A long-ago scene had come to me in my sleep that could put further discussion of the house to rest. If I lay there for enough time with my eyes open, I'd found, Rita was so sensitive she would invariably wake up. So I had hardly finished replaying the episode in my mind, when she asked me why I wasn't sleeping?

"I'd like to clear up a point," I said. "Think back to that time on the boat, the trip where Schif and I stole the lobsters—"

"I remember"—she interrupted,—"when you had such a rotten reputation. If we're going back *that* far, then I'd like to go back even further," she said. "Because lately, I've been thinking a lot about Harry Clork."

Since she had only seen him on that Christmas Eve when I scrubbed the floors at her house, I was flabbergasted that she remembered his name. She reminded me that Harry had told her of my writing talent, which had impressed him so much that he had decided to make me his collaborator. Rita was curious to know how I'd come to choose writing as my career, and what it was I had written that caught Harry's eye.

When I tried to evade her, she reminded me that when I had asked her how she started painting, she had told me about Utrillo. So she had every right to expect the same from me.

One of Rita's niftier gifts, she not only always looked beautiful—even at 2 A.M.—but she loved to go to the kitchen, bring back wine and cheese and fruit, and settle in for a good talk. So I told her how Harry had found me in the ranks of junior writers at Metro, a job that I got because of whom I knew, and not what I had written.

Harry had already become a hero to me, even before I ever met him, for an episode in his youth that had become studio legend. A friend of his was married to a famous singer named Nora Bayes. As life would have it, he had fallen in love with a younger woman. Not wanting to upset his wife's successful career, the husband turned to Harry Clork for advice. Harry convinced the husband of the importance of finding someone to fill his shoes—and not just his shoes, but his suits as well—so that Nora Bayes wouldn't notice any dramatic alteration in her lifestyle and start hitting sour notes.

After just a little looking around, Nora Bayes's husband discovered that Harry Clork was five foot three—precisely his size. So they exchanged coats and hats and shoes, and even aftershave lotion, and when the day was over it was as if they had been born twins and gotten somehow separated in the hospital nursery.

Naturally, no one appeared more surprised than Harry at this coincidence. But what testified to his strength of character was his behavior when the change of husbands took place. Nora Bayes never seemed to notice—never said a word, never hit a wrong note. And Harry did a splendid thing. He never mentioned it either.

So he became a famous writer, doing musicals on Broadway starring his new wife, Nora Bayes. But it wasn't too long, although Harry never said so, before he was looking for someone precisely his size who used the same aftershave.

When Harry called me into his office one day for an interview, I was so eager to rise from the rank of junior writer that I said all the wrong things. I knew I'd blown my chances of working with him, so I decided I might just as well ask him the question that was haunting me.

"Were you really *that* surprised, Mr. Clork, to discover you were the same size as Nora Bayes's husband, after you were the one who thought of finding someone to fill his shoes?"

Mr. Clork rose menacingly to his feet, which didn't make him any taller. But before he could throw me out, I found myself telling him how I'd been canvassing the sound stages in the hope I might come across a star's husband with a similar problem—a husband looking for the right size person to take his place. Now I'd come to him because I wanted to check out the complete *modus operandi* at the source.

It wasn't that I was dumb enough at nineteen to believe that such a thing really could happen again, I explained. But when you want so desperately to be a part of the studio world—not just a lowly junior writer who'd be better off shining shoes outside the commissary, so he might at least get to *talk* to the stars and directors—you begin to make yourself believe that just about anything in the way of miracles could happen.

Mr. Clork actually smiled. "No, I wasn't too surprised. I'd come to like him—because of our being the same size, that is. We saw things eye to eye."

I got the job working with Harry on the basis of that single encounter. I knew this was the last thing Rita had expected to hear. If my career had begun differently, I'm sure I would have shaded the truth to please her. But I wanted her to know my talent in the business hadn't been for writing. I had a flair for invention and construction, and that was it.

As long as I was clearing the air, I went on to what had made me wake up in the first place. I reminded her of the time we were sailing and of the dream she told me she'd had of me buying her a house. At the time I'd assured her I would make her dream a reality.

"I know I never mentioned that you might wind up paying for it," I admitted. "But the important thing was that I was going to get you a house, and you were so happy about it."

"You've forgotten," she said gently. "The house I dreamed of was on *wheels*," she said. "It was a tinker's house."

That only irritated me. "Then why'd you agree to buy our house when you saw it was earthbound?"

"You told me it would be a good investment," she said, and I could see the first flickerings of that Irish temper. "You said we'd have something to come home to in our old age."

"We will!"

"You didn't tell me that was *now*."

"Maybe we can get somebody to put some wheels under it," I said.

"I don't think I'd mind it so much," she said, after ignoring my inspiration, "if I was living with a writer, instead of a producer."

I didn't make any promises. I was smart enough to leave it there. But Rita wasn't. That was just another load of fuel to the fire smoldering inside her. It was like living with a volcano. I kept waiting for her to erupt. Harold got the idea of moving our whole operation to London for the shooting of *The Devil's Disciple*. Since Harold was producing, I wouldn't be all that busy, but more important, my gypsy would be out on the road again.

Beyond that, it would give me the opportunity to show that secret film footage from our wedding night. Coming right after her reviews for *Separate Tables*, it should ensure my getting the finances to ready the script I intended to direct for her. Overnight, everything went electric with excitement. All the trunks were out, and Rita was having a marvelous time giving orders like a general let loose in Times Square. Although I think she got her biggest high when she closed a deal to rent the house for twice what we'd expected. There's no greater thrill for a gypsy than to get paid to leave your house and hit the road.

The night before our sailing we got around to having my folks over. Rita had worked it out that way, because she knew it would offer the perfect excuse for that first hooker with my father and an accompanying toast to our departure. But my mother put it into clearer perspective. She offered a toast to the honeymoon we'd never had. And she was right. In all the time Rita and I had been together, we had never embarked on a great adventure.

Over dinner the three of them started talking about the kind of courage it takes to strike out on your own. It was then Rita told them that if I would make the move, she was sure she would have the courage to follow. My writing, her painting.

"There *is* no other true excitement," my father agreed, "until you're working to please yourself before you please anyone else."

Rita raised her wine glass to him. "Those were the very words I heard from your son on the first day I met him," she said. "I'll drink to that."

I raised my glass and drank as a hypocrite. All my energy was focused on setting up the picture with her. I figured I'd better lighten things up before they got *too* serious.

"I always think of that story of Noel Coward's. He said that after a couple of years of pleasing yourself, if you should suddenly discover that was all you were pleasing—then you'd better look for another trade." I waited, but there was not so much as a smile. So I quickly added, "I'd like to put away a little money first, so we won't have to worry about that."

My own mother dealt me the final blow. "Yes, dear," she said, "but I think all you men need a shove."

Rita perked right up. "You mean you had the same problem?"

"We were barely scraping out a living in Jeffersonville, Indiana. I was still carrying him," my mother said, nodding at me, "when his father had the chance to strike out on his own by moving the family to St. Louis."

The old man smiled. "You're not going to tell Rita about the model-T Ford?"

"Indeed I am," my mother said. "When he cranked it up, it would sometimes start and then pin him against the garage wall. That was when he'd holler for me."

"On the day she's talking about, I thought it was going right through me." The old man chuckled. "I was that helpless."

"He was also that uncertain about the move." My mother had the look of a conqueror. "I ran into the garage to help, but before I turned off the motor, I said, 'Make up your mind. Are we going to St. Louis, or aren't we?' He was gasping for breath, but he managed to say, 'St. Louis.' "

Everyone drank to that and Rita was radiant right through the rest of the evening.

Marriage to Rita made my mode of travel something I previously had associated only with royalty. I no longer walked through airports with the other peasants to board a plane. Instead, a limousine would drive us directly to the plane waiting on the runway. This provided Miss Hayworth with a private viewing, so that she could decide on exactly the seats she preferred.

I had never crossed the ocean on a luxury liner, so I felt an added thrill when we boarded the *United States* in New York. Once again we were whisked aboard in complete privacy. I got my next surprise when we entered our suite. I couldn't get over the immense living room, the well-stocked bar, plus an enormous velvet and silk bedroom. There were enough flowers to start a florist's shop. I had no sense of being aboard a ship, so throughout the crossing I was forever sticking my head out a porthole, just so I'd know we were really at sea.

The steward, who was unpacking our things, asked me where he should put a large cardboard box he'd taken from my suitcase. It was the film from our wedding night, that I had "forgotten" to tell Rita about.

"Oh, that," I said, all casualness. "Just toss it in one of those bottom drawers."

"You didn't forget it then?"

"Forget what?"

"The film."

She had never said a word.

"You knew I had the camera on?" I asked.

She nodded.

"And that I was filming all the time?"

"Of course."

"Why didn't you say something?"

"You were enjoying yourself too much."

I had to smile. "I should have guessed," I said. "You're amazing the way you always know."

"What are you going to do with it?"

"That's why I didn't tell you about it at the time," I said. "I was afraid it would inhibit your dancing and everything."

She smiled. "It never inhibited yours, so why should it have mine."

"Touché," I laughed, feeling much easier. "It was my intent to use it as the basis for a new vehicle to star you. Once I show it to the right people, financing it will be a cinch."

She was suddenly grave. "I've been thinking ever since that last dinner we had with your folks."

Immediately, I got a sinking feeling. "A lot of laughs," I said. "I don't remember anything serious enough for you to go all this serious on me."

"I've been thinking about that story your mother told."

"She made that up," I said.

"Your mother is no more capable of fabricating tales than I am. So I'm sure the story was true," she said, and I knew she was absolutely right. "But even if it wasn't, I've been coming to this decision for some time."

"What decision is that?" I said, as if I didn't know.

"I'm not going to make any more films."

"Just like that?"

"Just like that."

If ever I needed to put my head out of that porthole it was right then. "How are we going to pay for the house if you don't make *They Came to Cordura*?"

"You said you insured it."

"I did."

"We'll blow it up."

"You've got to quit saying that," I said, because each time she said it, she enjoyed the notion more.

"I'm serious."

I could see she was. "I don't care about *Cordura*, and I don't care about the house that much, either," I said. "But you've got to make this one picture for me, no matter what. It would be like Jack Nicklaus, with his natural golfing genius, never picking up a club."

She looked momentarily thoughtful, then her face lit up. "I'm not thinking, I guess," she said, picking up our empty glasses. "What's the matter with me?"

I can't begin to tell you how grateful I was to that fat kid for materializing that day at Pebble Beach. I began to feel a whole lot better.

Only when she returned, she was carrying not the refills, but a book on golfing in Scotland.

"There," she said, putting the open book in my hands, then turning the pages. "We'll start at St. Andrews and work our way back down to Glen Eagles."

If you're a member of royalty by default, because you rode in on the Queen's coattails, like that fellow who shares the throne in England, you have to learn patience. So with that in mind, I turned each of those pages in that book until we had that trip worked out to the last detail.

And the last detail for Rita was to say with that wicked gleam only she possessed, "We can't have too many golf balls, can we?"

"No," I agreed, bringing me to *my* last detail. "We're going to make that picture, Rita."

She still had the gleam. "We'll see."

One of the niftiest things about that trip was getting to spend so much time on the bridge, another privilege extended only to members of royalty. I had just left Rita at the hairdresser's and was on my way to the bridge when I heard a lovely voice speak my name. "Mr. Hill . . . ?" The voice matched the girl. "Mr. James Hill . . . ?"

She had that glorious English accent, like someone who had just been reviewing her vowels with Professor Rex Harrison. When I turned, I found an attractive young girl of nineteen or twenty looking intently up at me from her deep violet eyes.

"Yes, ma'am," I said.

Well, she went on to tell me that of all the films she had ever seen in her life, her very favorite was one I had produced, *The Sweet Smell of Success*. Now I wasn't about to disillusion her by telling her the picture had lost so much money it had just about landed our company in chapter 11. So I had to settle for the truth—the way I was trying to handle everything since my promise to Rita—by telling her it also happened to be *my* favorite. This so delighted her that she admitted she had never bought a man a drink in her life, but would like to buy me one now. Given her great good taste in films, it seemed sheer ingratitude to wreck her entire day by refusing her.

Anyway, we found two stools at the bar, and though it had been a while since I'd left Rita, I resolved not to be all the time checking my watch. A terribly rude thing, especially when the girl was so lovely. So I turned to her instead and she asked me in her wonderfully cultured English voice what I would like.

"I'd like an ice-cold dry martini," I said.

"Yes, that *would* be nice," another voice agreed.

Now there's no other voice like that in the whole world. At least, not in my world. So I need hardly tell you it belonged to Rita Hayworth, who was now seated on my other side.

If she had had a golf club in her hand, I would have feared for the portholes, but since she didn't, I started to introduce her, when I realized I didn't even know the lovely girl's name.

Well, Rita gave me a funny look, which didn't register at the time but should have, and in the very next breath, she was being charming. So we all had martinis and, though I kept waiting for the roof to fall in, or something worse, it never did. As unpredictable as only Rita could be, she was absolutely enchanting.

Maybe that's why I drank more than usual, even after we left that nice English film buff, had dinner, and spent some more time on our Scottish trip. So while I'd kept my guard up while we were awake, I learned one crucial thing when we went to bed. You can't afford to drop your guard, just because you've dropped the body.

I can only blame it on the rush of relief, what with Rita being so charming, and all the martinis and brandy that followed. Because I fell alseep immediately and found myself dreaming of that girl with the violet eyes and the nifty English vowels.

She had just made me an interesting proposition that would have solved my backing problems on the picture I planned for Rita and she was asking why I was hesitating, when, POW! Rita gave it to me right over the eye with the phone receiver. It was astonishing that she knew exactly who I was dreaming about. She said I hadn't fooled her for a minute when I pretended not to know the English girl's name, since I had clearly been with her every time I'd told her I'd been on the bridge.

So that had been my first mistake. The next was ever having allowed myself to dream of her in the first place. Anyway, while Rita called the doctor, I made yet an even bigger error. She was fighting tears at what she had done—what with the blood on my forehead and her being so contrite and all—but I couldn't stop laughing.

I told her that in my dream the English girl had just offered me all the money I needed to develop our picture. It was the best deal I'd ever heard of—then *she* had to wreck it.

"Yes, but what did she want in return?" Rita said, giving me her wicked look. "She wanted you, didn't she!" Rita exploded. "And don't tell me you weren't going to take her up on the deal!"

"Well, not me so much," I said, pretending modesty, "as my body."

Luckily, it was right about then that the doctor arrived because Rita was reaching for something to throw. I drank another brandy in order to make his job easier. It saved him having to worry about anesthetic. The doctor had to take five stitches, but what concerned him more than that was the way I couldn't stop laughing.

It was the next day, when we were due to dock at Southampton, that the significance of Rita's gift for extrasensory perception really hit me. Not only did I have to be careful who I was thinking about from now on, but who I dreamed about, as well.

I had a big bandage over my eye, and Rita was contrition incarnate —she couldn't do enough for me—which made it all worthwhile. Although what worried her even more was the purser, who arrived to tell her a flotilla of newsmen were coming aboard. As soon as we were alone again, I realized it wasn't the presence of the media, but what I might tell them about the bandage that was bothering her. So I told her I was going to tell them the truth. I reminded her how I'd made her that promise never to lie again in her presence, and now was no time to go back on my word.

"You'd never sleep nights," she said, "if you told the truth."

"Watch me."

"You wouldn't dare!"

I shrugged, pretending to feel sorry for myself as I ran a finger over the bandage. "You said you weren't going to make the picture with me. You said you weren't even going to make *Cordura*. So what difference?"

She sighed, and when she sighed like that it made me want to do just about anything for her.

"I don't *believe* you'd really tell them," she said.

I had to smile. "Wouldn't I?"

"Not about your dream of that English girl." When I didn't say anything, but just continued to smile, she went on. "That would be bad enough, but to tell them about the telephone, and your eye, *that* would be unforgivable. You should never talk about such intimate family matters."

"You'll see," I said.

"I'd never speak to you again, if you did."

When the purser came to escort us to the lounge we found all the media waiting. There were several other well-known personalities there when we came in. But once the journalists spotted Rita, it was adieu to all the rest.

They must have asked a million questions, yet Rita never lost her cool. I had long since been elbowed out of the way, when one of the shorter members of the Fleet Street fraternity who had suffered a similar fate, eased up alongside me.

"You know anything about that new husband she has aboard?" this crafty-looking little guy said, staring up at me. "I'd like to run the poor bastard down, because I'm not getting anything fresh out of *her*."

Naturally, I'd been looking for just such an opening, so I glanced around cautiously before lowering my voice. "I heard the poor bastard suffered some kind of unusual accident because of another woman," I said. "I was planning to ask Miss Hayworth about that myself."

It worked perfectly. By the time he had tunneled his way through the crowd, I had elbowed my way alongside her.

"I have it from a reliable source," the little bastard said, "that your new husband suffered an unusual and serious accident, because of another woman."

I can't begin to tell you the relief in Rita's eyes when she found me standing beside her. She hugged my arm tight to her, and whispered into my ear. "I'll do the picture, I'll do *anything*, if you'll just get me out of this." Then she turned to the others. "I thought everyone knew my husband."

Obviously, the little reporter didn't. "Hey!" he exclaimed, as it hit him that I was his reliable source. "What the hell's going on here?"

"I've always been an admirer of the English press," I said, even though I'd promised Rita I would never lie again in her presence. "So I'm naturally shocked at such an unfounded and rude question."

"Something screwy's going on," he said. "What about your eye?"

"She hit me," I said. "Isn't *that* what you wanted to hear?"

Everyone roared, which meant no one believed me. It was the perfect excuse for us to make our exit. So I took her arm and started easing her out, as I said to the others, "We can't thank you enough for your wonderful fairness and all the trouble you've gone to in coming out here."

Rita seconded me and they gave her a nifty hand. The last thing I remember seeing in that lounge was the frustrated face of that pint-sized reporter. I almost wanted to go back and thank him.

Our arrival at the Savoy Hotel was transformed into a celebration. They had redecorated one of their river suites for Rita. I don't know how they knew, but they had done it in all her favorite colors. It was like rediscovering our cave. Not only did the suite have a bar tucked off in a corner, but it had a magnificent beamed, high-ceilinged living room overlooking the Thames. Even more important, it had a splendid fireplace with a never-ending supply of knotty wood. And you never had to worry about getting it cold by turning the thermostat down, because it never really got all that warm in London.

Throughout our stay I was focused on one thing—how to properly unveil the film I had taken of her the night of our wedding. It was important that a few of the money people saw it, along with such major talents as Sir Carol Reed, so that we could not only raise the financing to ensure its development, but snare the creative types to guarantee its production.

Naturally, the obvious thing would have been to give a big cocktail party, then invite the select few who showed genuine interest to a private screening. But as always, and especially after the rigors of that shipboard press conference, Rita was against that. So I was wracking my brain for another approach.

Meanwhile, our cave was proving to be even more private than the original, which couldn't have made Rita happier. It was customary for us to have the hotel switchboard screen incoming calls. The Savoy took it upon themselves to guard Rita's privacy with a vengeance. Not a call came through; they merely took messages. And since I never thought to pick them up, absolutely no one was able to get in touch with us.

I don't know how long this might have gone on if I hadn't seen Bernie Kamber lurking in the lobby. Bernie, you'll recall, was not only the vice-president and head of our publicity department, but he was even dearer to my heart because of his roving crockery. So instead of going to my meeting, I went right back up to our suite to tell Bernie's tragic tale of our being incommunicado to Rita. I also, of course, had an ulterior motive—something I'm beginning to realize I had every time I made a move during this period.

In retrospect I guess that that, as much as anything, helped screw everything up. If you're going to be rash enough to give up lying, you should plan on abandoning ulterior motives as well, because one is just about as bad as the other.

Anyway, I began by telling her how desperately Bernie had been trying to get in touch with me for Harold, which meant that everyone else who felt close to us must have been experiencing the same frustration. Harold's case was even more dire, though, because of the problems they were having with the shooting of *The Devil's Disciple*, in which Burt was starring. When Harold hadn't been able to reach me by phone, he hadn't even bothered to unpack. Instead, he had told Bernie that the company's fate could depend on his getting in touch with me immediately. So Bernie told Harold he would come right over and hang around the lobby of the Savoy, because sooner or later, one of us would be bound to be going out to the chauffeured Rolls-Royce to pick up our regulation Dom Perignon and caviar from Fortnum & Mason.

Well, Harold blew up at poor old Bernie. He swore at him something fierce. How *could* a corporate officer contemplate doing such a menial thing? Anyone who couldn't think of a more clever solution, he told him, should not only be demoted to carrying Harold's bags like any ordinary porter, but unpacking them as well.

Harold went on to remind Bernie that since he was now vice-president in charge of advertising and publicity, he should begin to think like one. The first thing any vice-president would do, Harold informed him, would be to send me a telegram.

Well, once Bernie had done all that—phoned it down to the desk and all—Harold showed how pleased he was.

"Bernie," Harold said, "*now* you can unpack my bags."

So he not only wound up unpacking Harold's bags, but he got blamed because I never answered the telegram which, needless to say, wound up with all those other undelivered messages.

Rita sighed, one of those real sad sighs. "Poor old Bernie," she said. "If only we'd been taking our calls, we could have spared him all that humiliation."

It wasn't just Bernie, I told her, but all our other friends who were even closer to us whom we must have offended. I didn't think she was getting the point, but then her face brightened.

"Why don't we have a cocktail party and invite everyone we might have offended?" she asked.

"I think it would be swell," I said.

"Except producers," she added. "No producers, even *if* they feel offended." She gave me her most enigmatic smile.

Anyway, that's what I meant by the ulterior motive business, because I had achieved exactly what I wanted in the first place. And when you're dealing with someone as honest as Rita, who has such trusting eyes and can also sigh like that, dissembling may, in fact, be worse than lying.

To tell you the absolute truth about that cocktail party, it was a monumental success—and for all the wrong reasons.

In the days preceding it I worried about Rita, and how she would fill up her time. The last thing I wanted was for her to be uptight on the night of the party, as only she could get if she had nothing else to preoccupy her. More of my days than I'd expected were spent working on various scripts our company had in development. So I really saw very little of her until dinner every evening.

I needn't have worried on that account. No one could fill their days better than Rita. I was amazed at the way she haunted the booksellers —Hatchard's, Foyles, Blackwell's—and her interest in silver and antiques. Simply listening to her accounts of the Tate, the National Gallery and all the private art galleries she visited was providing me a secondhand education. And with all that, she managed her days so adroitly that she got in some golf and some painting, as well.

Astonishingly, she suggested that I show the film at the party. Since I'd planned to use the occasion to cull the proper guests for a later screening, and since *she* innocently thought the party was to make amends to all those we might have offended, I took her up on it immediately.

As you can imagine, all the right people were there—the money men, as well as the major talents I respected—men like Nunnally Johnson, Carol Reed, and Terence Rattigan.

Rita kept reminding me that we should at least invite *one* person whom we might have offended, since that was the reason for the party. So I suggested she ask old Bernie, since he'd suffered the most on our behalf.

Now I had taken the time to review the first reel of that film footage, and it was so good I hadn't bothered running the rest. Rita and her castanets. She was wearing a gaucho outfit with a broad-brimmed black sombrero, and she was stomping and whirling all over the living room of our apartment, as only she could.

I could actually *feel* that audience responding to the first touches of comedy, as she began to burlesque her own flamenco siren routine. *If they think that's something*, I said to myself, *wait until they see her really cut loose in the next reel.* Then I heard a chuckle.

When I resolved to film Rita clandestinely, you'll recall, I had made up my mind that I didn't want her drinking so much she would forget what she'd done come next morning. So whenever she paused in her routines, I would replenish our drinks. Then, after she started dancing again, I would sneak her drink back and drink most of it myself.

That was what had happened at the end of the first reel to provoke that curious chuckle. It never entered my mind that anyone would imagine I was actually *stealing* her drinks, but I guess someone did. It sent a sort of chill through me. It truly did.

Once we got into the next reel, the one I *hadn't* looked at, I seemed to be drinking her drink every other minute, and—what with downing all my own—pretty soon I was dancing along with her. Of course by now the footage was beginning to look like one of those old speeded-up Laurel and Hardy's. And everyone in the audience was roaring.

Things kept getting worse for me, because the faster I drank, the faster I danced, and the harder all our guests laughed—and *no* one was enjoying it more than Rita.

If that wasn't enough, I had to watch myself doing the old soft shoe with her. It wasn't so much my clumsiness, but I was beginning to weave a bit from drinking for two. And even with someone as graceful and as coordinated as Rita—a veritable feather afloat in a breeze—I posed a direct threat to her physical well-being by stomping around her that way. Talk about the old soft shoe!

Then came the most embarrassing moment of all. It's even hard to write about now—emotion recollected in tranquility—because I stopped us in midflight, as though we had just been given a spontaneous ovation. And to acknowledge it, instead of an understatedly elegant bow, I picked up a golf club. Then I proceeded to knock out every window in our apartment as I drove one golf ball after another, while Rita stood there applauding.

So, as I said, the evening turned into a blockbuster for the wrong reasons. Every one of those money men, along with all the talent—even old Bernie—everybody but everybody was still laughing hysterically as they took their leave.

And worse than that, all the birds were singing the same tune: "At least we know who the comedian is in *that* family."

After everyone had gone, Rita was exhausted and I felt like a zombie. So when she went right to bed, I sat on, drinking and watching the lights of the tugs and barges on the Thames, somehow envying them. They looked so warm and snug and purposeful, as though their captains not only knew exactly where they were going, but were going there in style. Not me. Here I was married to the world's most beautiful comedienne, and in trying to let people in on my secret, I'd managed to run aground. Talk about boxing the old compass!

Rita was wonderfully relaxed the next day. She had taken it for granted that I knew exactly what was on that second reel of film. So when I had shown it, she felt that I was simply sharing the joke with everyone else. It was as if that had put period to the whole comedienne business.

Anyway, she had made one of her rare dates to be interviewed that afternoon because she had a great deal of respect for the man who was to do the piece. Kenneth Tynan was not only a prominent figure in the London theatrical world, but he was also a highly capable journalist. And though I had never spent any time with him, I was grateful that he was coming by.

Beyond that, it gave me the excuse to retire to the park behind the Savoy. I was still trying to collect myself after the previous evening's debacle. It wasn't so much a park, but a strip of grass that ran along the rear of the Savoy and the other buildings fronting on the Strand. But it faced the Thames, and had benches and not many people, so it was an ideal place for daydreaming. I don't know how long I'd been sitting there when who should materialize but Kenneth Tynan.

"I was hoping I might get lucky and find you here," he said.

I asked him how the interview went. He sort of smiled and shook his head. He said this was the second time he'd spent a good couple of hours with Rita, and while there was no one in films he found more gracious, she always eluded him. Once he walked away, he would discover he knew no more about her than he did before they met. I nodded my agreement—invitation enough for him to sit down beside me on the bench. While I knew he was doing it to get background information for his piece, I found myself welcoming the chance to talk about her.

Now in all my years with Rita, this was the only time I ever did such a thing. Why I should have talked so intimately with a virtual stranger puzzles me till this day. But there was something about Tynan that made me feel his interest in her went beyond a mere magazine profile. I mean not only did he share my admiration for her, but like me, he felt there was untapped greatness there.

"What do you think makes a superstar?" he opened. "I'm talking about in films."

"I don't think it has much to do with acting," I replied.

"Very little," he said. "Although in Rita's case, she has the potential to be a *great* actress."

"You really think so?" I asked.

"I don't think so, I know it," he said. "She has the potential to be anything she wants."

I can't tell you what it meant to hear someone of his experience say that, because I was beginning to think that being so close to her might have somehow blinded me. And when I asked what it was he found in her that set her apart from all the others, he mirrored my thoughts, almost word for word.

"She smolders. No matter how calm she appears in a scene, she makes you feel there's something down inside her that's smoldering."

I told him that was what had so captivated me when I first saw her in *Gilda*. It was as if a series of tiny eruptions were forever taking place. But what kept me on the edge of my seat was my sense that there had to be a big one coming up—and that big one stood to blow the whole lid from here to kingdom come.

"Mount Etna," he said, nodding. "I can even feel it when I'm sitting in a room with her. It's what draws me to her. Especially when I contrast it to that incredible surface calm of hers."

Then he went on to say he saw her whole involvement with acting as a love-hate relationship. In one breath she hated the pretense, the phoniness of it, which was why she wanted to walk away—but in the next, in order to survive she needed the stimulation acting provided.

Maybe I should have told him that what he said about her relationship to her work also held true in her life. She wanted a full life, yet she wanted none of the obligations that entailed. So in the end, she could only feel that necessary respite from herself when she was on the move. Like the gypsies.

But I didn't know Tynan well enough to go into any of that, much as I'd have liked to. It sure made life a funny thing to contemplate: The constant turbulence Rita had to live with—and that she'd be the first to want to be rid of—was the very thing that gave her greatness in everything she did.

Anyway, I eventually got to her talent for comedy, which didn't surprise Tynan at all. But, I asked him, if someone has a gift like that, does a friend have the right to press them to reveal it?

"You're talking about something rarer than rubies, when you talk about a woman as beautiful as Rita being so blessed," he said.

"I know, but it didn't seem to surprise you."

"Nothing would surprise me about Rita's potential," he said. "So when you talk about her having a great comedic talent, I'm willing to bet on it."

"But she does have that love-hate relationship with her work to begin with. So is it *right* to press her?"

"Absolutely!" he said. "My God, how often do you suppose Fred Astaire's mother booted him around when he was a kid? Or Diaghilev and the greatest artist of them all, Nijinsky. When you find that sort of talent in someone like Rita, you can't let up on it!"

I felt all the old excitement returning. Here was Kenneth Tynan, who hardly knew Rita, and he was on his feet—that carried away—just by talking about her.

The sun was finally going down when we said goodbye, and I have to admit I've never felt better. I no longer had the slightest doubt about what I saw in our future.

A few days later, the lights were coming on aboard the barges as they plied their way up and down the Thames. I had started the fire in the fireplace, while Rita was reading Tynan's profile of her that had appeared that day.

"I think he knows more about me than I do about myself." She thought for a moment, then smiled that secret smile. "Did *you* know that much about me?"

I had the feeling she knew we'd done some talking. She always seemed to know about such things. I didn't say anything, being more interested in what she would reveal next.

"I love the notion of those little volcanos going off inside, that he says he senses in me when he sees me on the screen."

I had to smile. "I have the same feeling, and it's not limited to your performance on screen," I said.

She went back to studying the profile. "I'm not sure whether I agree with him or not," she said, frowning as she read on.

"About what?"

"His feeling that if you have a talent, you have no right to hide it. I think a gift is an intensely private matter. You shouldn't have to exploit it, if you don't want to."

"I disagree. Talent of any kind is far too rare. I think it's selfishness to hide it. Especially when a person might become another Renoir or a Mozart."

"If they stood to become a Renoir or a Mozart, I'm inclined to agree," she said. "But just to be a film personality, I don't know . . ."

As long as she hadn't closed her mind, I had hope. So as we continued to watch the night descend on the river below, I mixed some drinks and offered a suggestion.

"Why don't we take a look at the political future of the planet. Then when we get to Scotland for golf, we'll be better equipped to continue this discussion?" I said. "Have you ever thought of taking the global view?"

"No, but I think I'd like to," she said. She was amused but interested, because she put on her glasses—something she rarely did unless it was important to her. So as farfetched as all this may sound, it's only because I haven't mentioned any of the following:

First, there was the Berlin Film Festival, for which she'd been asked to serve as honorary chairman. By personal invitation of the head of the West German government, Willy Brandt.

Second, an art festival in Paris had asked that she make an appearance, to be followed by afternoon tea in their country home at the invitation of President and Mrs. Charles de Gaulle.

Third, there was a dinner invitation from Chris Mann, who had a farm bordering Winston Churchill's. We were asked to come early, because Mr. Churchill was so ardent a fan of Rita's he had expressed a desire to have her join him at his home for drinks.

Fourth, there was our own American ambassador to the Court of St. James's, Jock Whitney. He had requested Rita's presence as the guest of honor at a flag-raising ceremony.

"Imagine your effect on Charles de Gaulle," I said.

"I'm trying," she said, "but I'm not seeing any."

"You've got to use your imagination," I explained. "he's talking to the most enticing woman in the world who's hanging on his every word. And her only concern is why the little children in Africa are so thin."

"What if he doesn't think I'm all that enticing?" she said. "After all, you're prejudiced, because you think I'm funny."

"I'm not *that* prejudiced, but I know if you speak a little French, he's got to be vulnerable. He's been married to the same woman forever."

Once again, I might have made things easier if I had leveled with Rita. I knew there was no better way to raise the backing for our picture than from the financial men who surrounded prominent figures. Jock Whitney alone might do. After all, he'd been the prime backer of David O. Selznick when he made *Gone With the Wind*.

Rita had already met and liked Whitney, so I couldn't have been more pleased than I was when she decided on making his occasion her initial visit.

"It'll be a chance to see if my glasses are strong enough," Rita said, "before I attempt the global view!"

The flag-raising ceremony at the American Embassy proved to be an enormous lawn party. Mr. Whitney saw to it that Rita didn't have to leave the privacy of his living quarters until the actual ceremony, and then it only lasted half an hour or so.

Prior to that, Mr. Whitney had taken us into his private bar for drinks. Rita clearly felt at ease with him, but that didn't explain a side of her I'd never seen before. She had often brought up the subject of underprivileged children, but with Mr. Whitney, she launched into the problem that American enlisted men faced at outlying bases in England where they didn't have proper educational facilities for their families. Where she had got her information, I had no idea. But before I knew it, she had Mr. Whitney pulling out a pad and pen, and taking notes.

While he was busy doing that, she ostentatiously put on her half-glasses and looked mischievously over them at me.

We went into the living room, where there were a number of other notables, including Fred Astaire. That was when I saw yet another side of Rita. She was expert at fixing toupees that had gone askew. Once she had adjusted Fred's, they seemed to have a million things to say to each other. It was that kind of reunion, dating all the way back to *You Were Never Lovelier*, that gave me the perfect opportunity to go over my plans with Mr. Whitney. When I outlined the comedy debut I had in mind for Rita, he couldn't have been more receptive.

We were both hungry when we finally managed to break away. We were also proud of our separate accomplishments, so we decided on a small celebration. There was a restaurant in Soho we had been to once and liked. It was such a beautiful night we excused our driver and walked through the peaceful twilight streets of London.

There were very few diners in the restaurant, so we managed to slip into a booth unobserved. The restaurant had a reputation for its splended sole, the greatest dish in all London. What with a bottle of mello white burgundy, not to mention the candle glow, it turned into a summit banquet. Rita settled on the date for seeing Sir Winston Churchill, as well as Willy Brandt and the Berlin Film Festival, and we decided we'd wind up with a trip to Paris and the De Gaulles.

It was on this heady level of men-of-affairs that we left the restaurant. I was aware of moving past a number of people outside, but they seemed to be caught up in conversation. Then someone spoke the word Gilda.

In the very next breath, we were surrounded—with everybody shouting "Gilda," "Rita," and "It's Rita Hayworth." In the past, when a crowd gathered, they waited patiently for autographs. But this time, they acted as if they wanted to touch her, or carry her away. I don't know *what* they wanted. The whole street was suddenly dense with people.

I kept a firm grip in Rita's hand, but there was no way we could move, other than with the crowd. If they should start to panic, I knew we were lost. It was like being caught in a riptide. If you didn't anticipate and move with it, you were doomed. Once we guessed wrong, and Rita started to fall. Somehow I managed to lift her back up. The second time, her sheer weight dragged me down with her. For a moment, I thought she'd fainted. her face was whiter than white. But miracle of miracles, the next surge of the crowd brought us back to our feet.

More than anything, I was afraid Rita might scream. That would be the spark it would take to ignite the crowd. Their voices had remained ominously low as they chanted her name, interspersing it with "Gilda, Gilda." The rumble of an approaching train.

I was barely managing to hold her up by now and I knew it was only a matter of minutes before I collapsed from the tension and sheer exhaustion.

Then we heard whistles, and a voice over a loudspeaker. The police had arrived. The crowd melted away as fast as they had appeared. I'll never know how Rita managed to keep her poise through that terrifying few minutes. I only know in my whole life, I have never been that terrified.

It was also the only time in my life I ever saw her look disheveled. I mean, she could be scrubbing floors, or deeply absorbed with her palette and canvas, and she always looked elegant. It wasn't the smudges on her face, or her torn clothes, but the trauma of what she had been through that made her hand so icy in mine.

We were in the car of the chief of police. He kept praising Rita's calm and fortitude. I don't think he was aware she spoke not one word in that entire ride back to the Savoy. I remember what most impressed me about him—he didn't ask for an autograph.

The first thing I did when we got to our suite was pour us a brandy. The first thing Rita did was take her snifter and head straight for the shower. It was so like her to try to erase any trace of a traumatic experience by washing it off.

I tried to talk about it, in the hope she would, but it didn't work. Then I returned to our dinner conversation—to all her happy plans for the future—but nothing I said would draw her out. Other than a nod, or an occasional yes or no, she never said a word.

It was the middle of the night when she woke up screaming, "I hate it!"

When I tried to calm her she looked right through me. No matter how hard I worked to explain that she was safe—that the incident was behind her—she never heard me. She just kept screaming those three words.

I had called the desk immediately for a doctor. He arrived in the next few minutes, but it wasn't until he had given her a sedative that she began to calm down.

Once she'd fallen asleep, her hand curled in her hair like an exhausted child, I could see that he wanted to talk, but I didn't. He was quick to realize that. But unlike the police chief, he ran true to form —he left me the name of his daughter for an autograph.

St. Andrews gave us a profound sense of *déjà vu*. I don't know how many times I'd seen their Royal and Ancient Golf Club photographed by friends who'd played and written us from there. And we'd seen their opening and closing holes on television time and again. But finally to see it in person was about fifty times more enchanting than either of us had ever imagined.

There was the quaint old town, two- and three-story frame houses, all set on a rise and fronting the sea. With its narrow, winding lanes and mellow gray houses, the town looked as though it had been there forever. But what really astonished us was that when we arrived, close to midnight, it was still light. People were even out on the course playing golf. *That* was how far north we were.

We'd taken the Royal Scot out of London that morning, then a chauffeured car had met us at the Edinburgh station. We could have changed to another train and continued to St. Andrews, but we liked the idea of driving the rest of the way. So there we were, settled into one of those ancient houses on the top floor, in a lovely suite that had a warmth we had never experienced before or since. It was like living in our own little farmhouse, though not many farmers would have had such a nifty bar with a roaring fire going when they staggered home. Leaded-glass windows overlooked the golf course and beyond it the sea. Our host had set out a table laden with a variety of cheeses and cold cuts. No members of royalty ever had a finer welcome.

How strange that twenty-four hours earlier, we had been going through the nightmare crush of that crowd! I knew Rita must be thinking the very same thing. She hadn't referred to it, not once, even though I'd tried to draw her out. So it came as a welcome surprise over dinner when she finally brought it up.

"I don't blame those people," she said, her voice soft and without rancor. "If I enjoyed the image they think of as me, then I'd enjoy *them*. But I don't." There was a long pause. "I hate it!"

I had never heard her raise her voice, until the night when she cried out in that nightmare. Now for the first time, I knew what she meant. For the first time I realized how completely she despised the image of the Love Goddess the studio had created for her.

"I understand," I said.

I was too elated that she had finally brought the incident out into the open to risk further discussion. But I also knew in my heart that together we could change that image, if Rita would just give herself the chance.

In retrospect, I realize that it never entered my mind that she was saying anything larger. Even if she had been, I still wouldn't have believed her. Here she was with the world at her feet, and I just couldn't imagine her wanting something as simple as just to be herself. Not the girl who was born Margarita Carmen Cansino.

Once I decided I had the solution, I made up my mind to devote myself to making this the most memorable holiday she had ever experienced. It was hard to believe, but so much of the summer had already slipped away. There were only four weeks left before it would be time for her to return to Los Angeles to start shooting *They Came to Cordura*.

It was an enchanted month. What with golfing all the famous Scots courses and her painting and our forays into that peerlessly lovely countryside of purple moors and brooding lochs and ruined castles, before we knew it we were at the final stop on our agenda, Glen Eagles.

We wound up with a suite there that almost outdid the one at the Savoy. Up until then we'd thought we were roughing it—if you can tour the country in a Daimler limousine with some ten suitcases and still think of it that way—but Glen Eagles was the quintessence of sophistication and elegance.

We were out on the golf course our first day when I heard someone call my name. It was Neil Paterson, a fine writer who had recently written the script for *Room at the Top*. Neil previously had done some work for our company back in Los Angeles, so it was like old home week running into him, and an added surprise to discover that he had his home right there in Glen Eagles.

We played together every day after that, and I could see that Rita was enjoying him just as much as I was. The night before we left, Neil invited us to his house for dinner. Rita never liked to do any socializing on our last few days in a place, but this time she startled me by accepting eagerly.

Well, that was my introduction to the typical British dinner party. There were four other married couples, beside Neil and his wife, but the women were as good as invisible. No one asked a woman's opinion about anything. The real topper came after dinner. All the men adjourned into one room, while the women went into another. Only the big difference between the two rooms was that the men had all the booze—and Dow '23 vintage port it was, at that—and the women just had one another.

If I'd had any idea Rita was in there with all those women she'd never met before, without so much as a sustaining drink, I know I'd never have had that first port.

Quickly we got into some pressing masculine matters, like recent Scots soccer victories. This led to a round of victory toasts that were sung, which brought on more singing, and I couldn't help thinking —now I was one of them—what a wonderful *esprit de corps* these grand chaps had. And to think I'd found it by such a lucky chance, running into Neil the way I had.

Well, that's about *all* I remember of that evening, except for running off the road while driving back to the hotel, since I'd given the chauffeur the night off. That was the first thing that hit me the next morning. And then I got really worried, because I remembered Rita's old terror of driving.

It was our last day at Glen Eagles, and she didn't say a word about the previous evening's debacle. Her very forbearance made everything about twice as bad. So just as we planned, we went out to play golf, and all I was praying for was that some little thing might happen that would give me the chance to somehow begin to make things right with her. Like a miracle.

Among the delights of Glen Eagles were our two caddies. Wherever we went, people could never do enough for Rita once they recognized her—which they could do, it seemed, at fifty paces while looking at the back of her head. If I'm to be absolutely honest, those two caddies had more to do than anyone in bringing off the miracle I'd been hoping for.

They were both well into their eighties, but they were celebrities in their own right. One had caddied for the greatest of all English golfers, Harry Vardon. The other had not only carried Walter Hagen's clubs when he won the British Open, but had joined him in a number of celebratory drinking bouts. So nearly as many people clustered around them as around Rita when we teed off.

It bothered me that first day—I mean at their ages, those old gents having to carry our clubs. But they clearly loved their work and always showed up immaculately dressed with vests and ties, and even wearing hats, which was how good caddies always dressed in those vintage days of Vardon and Hagen.

My difficulty was that I couldn't understand a word either of them said. It wasn't that they spoke Gaelic. I just couldn't penetrate their Scots burrs. And what made it even worse, they couldn't understand me either.

On the other hand, they came through crystal clear to Rita, and she to them. So, in effect, she acted as our interpreter. But there were still times when I was at a distance from her, when I'd ask for a putter and wind up with a driver instead.

It was misting the morning when we started out on our final round, and the visibility got dimmer as we moved along. By the time we'd finished the front 9, we were practically the only ones left on the course.

Ordinarily, we would have knocked off because there were wisps of fog creeping in, too, but all of us were aware of how well Rita was playing. Since she didn't hit the ball long enough off the tee like a man, it meant she had to take one extra stroke to get to each of the par 4 holes.

So when I tell you that par was 36 and she had shot a 44, that meant she had shot a near-perfect 9. If she could do the same on the back 9, she would have broken 90—something she'd never done before or even come close to. And on that course, in that kind of weather, I guarantee very few women could have equaled her score. Not too many men, for that matter. So in a sense, history was in the making, or that requested miracle.

If you haven't already guessed, those two old codgers caddying for us were cap-over-golf-bags in love with her. And not because she was who she was, but because she never made excuses, no matter what the weather, and of course—even more important to them—because of the lovely rhythm of her swing.

"Just like Harry," one would say in his heavy burr, "even to his grip."

Then a little bit later, the other one would say, "I only wish Walter was here, lass. He only liked women when he was drinking, but he'd like you, lass, when you're swinging. And I mean with a golf club."

Then they'd both cackle gleefully.

On this particular day, I couldn't have been more grateful for their chatter, because it was that kind of talk that kept her loose. The tension was building, mostly in the three watching her, though I could already tell that it would be just about the biggest thing in her life so far if she did break 90.

When we arrived at the eighteenth tee, she hit her first poor drive of the day. Not that she didn't catch it flush, but she pulled it, so it ricocheted off the trees to the left. She had to get a 5 on this hole to make family history, so when we couldn't find the ball at first, we

thought for sure her chances were nil. It meant hitting another drive
from the tee, where she would be lying 3, with only two shots left to
get down in. Practically an impossibility.

Those two old codgers wouldn't quit looking, though. And son-
ofagun, if one of them didn't find that elusive ball. It was a real break,
too, because it had kicked off the hill, and she had gotten an additional
40 yards of roll.

The rain was really pelting down by now, which was bad enough.
But worse, there were about 500 people on the verandah of the clubhouse overlooking the eighteenth green—all of them out there to
watch Rita.

When we'd made the turn, someone outside our group had heard
us talking about her score. Word had spread, and a crowd had gathered to see if Rita Hayworth could break 90.

One of the things that has always fooled people about Rita,
she was always shy when she was expected to do something she
hadn't done to perfection in private. Like the miracle of breaking 90.

So all that kept her from picking up and walking away were those
two old caddies. "You can do it, lass," they just kept saying, over and
over, like they were gentling a thoroughbred, "smooth and easy."
And the next thing, they had a 4 iron in her hand, since it was a good
130 yards to the green. With all the rain and everything, the air was
really heavy.

If I'd had any faith in the power of prayer, I would have offered
one up right then. Instead, I just sort of hunched deeper into my
windbreaker and watched her take that club back.

Well, it was as perfect as any golf swing you've ever seen on the
ladies' tour. She had a narrow opening through the trees and then
some traps to clear, and as if it had eyes, that little old ball did all
those things. Then it took a couple of gentle bounces, and wound up
five feet from the pin.

She didn't show it much on the outside, but I've never sensed her
feeling happier inside, because that crowd kept applauding her all the
way up to that green. If she hadn't reined herself in, we'd have
probably carried her on our shoulders, those two caddies and I. We
were busting a gut, we were that proud. But she was so feminine and

dignified, with that skater's glide of hers, we just didn't dare do anything flamboyant.

Anyway, Rita really put the frosting on the cake, because she stepped up and stroked that ball right into the hole. Not only had she broken 90, she had shot an 87. She birdied that final hole.

That crowd went crazy. It was pouring now, but nobody seemed aware of it, the way they swarmed her for autographs. But what I remembered most vividly, next to her score, as I told her later, was the way those two old codgers were signing autographs like crazy, too. You talk about summoning up the ghosts of Harry Vardon and Walter Hagen! Well, she had surely done *that* for them.

When she finally managed to get free of it all, who should we bump into but Bob Hope. "What do you have to do to attract a crowd like that?" he said.

"It all starts by getting the right caddies," Rita said, and while she was smiling, I knew she meant it.

I didn't know, until we got back to our suite, that she'd invited the two old gents and their wives to dinner. It was remarkable—one of them had been married for sixty-two years and the other sixty-four. I couldn't imagine anyone living that long, never mind with the same woman. It was all I could do not to ask Rita whether she thought they still did it? Ever since that incident on the *United States*, though, when I got the phone receiver over the eye, I've been wary of anything she might construe as having Freudian overtones. So I curbed my curiosity.

They were all dressed up in their finest, but the wives had Scots burrs even thicker than their husbands, so Rita had to do the interpreting as usual.

She had dinner served in our suite, and when it was over, we followed the British custom: the women and the men separated. Only this time Rita saw to it that she and the two wives went into the room where the liquor was, leaving the three of us out there in the desert.

Before long, we began to hear singing from the bar. It was Bobby Burns's "The Bonnie Banks of Loch Lomond." If I could just have understood anything those two old codgers were saying, our predicament might not have gotten to me. But what with being Scotchless in Scotland, I decided the joke was over.

The door to the bar was locked. If that wasn't bad enough, those two old codgers started chuckling. I had the feeling they'd really begun wondering how Rita had come to marry me in the first place. It wasn't just my lousy golf, but who wouldn't laugh at a husband who couldn't even get a drink.

So I backed up, and when they saw I was going to break that door down with my shoulder, they stopped snickering. For the first time, I could see I'd won their respect. Just as I was about to start my rush, the singing stopped abruptly, the door was flung open, and out came the women bearing drinks for all of us.

I'll never forget the mischievous look on Rita's face. She didn't say anything, but her eyes told me she was enjoying this final triumph nearly as much as her 87.

Later that same night I woke up and found her reading. She was *still* trying to finish *They Came to Cordura*.

"What woke you up in the first place?" I said.

"I'll only tell you if you promise to be serious."

"If I'm serious," I said, "I'll only bore you, and you'll go back to sleep."

"Have you ever thought about having a child?" she asked me.

Now I should have realized that she was still elated at her triumph on the golf course. And in her reticent way, she was offering to share the ultimate in victory. Only at that moment it was the very last thing I expected. So I started to make a joke, until I saw how serious she was.

"Wouldn't you like a child?" she persisted.

Well, I had to admit I had no ready answer. It suddenly hit me how blithely people went about having children, almost as a matter of course. As if they were expected to, if they wanted to be thought of as having a serious marriage.

I told her I couldn't imagine having a child, what with the world in such precarious shape to begin with. Unless parents could guarantee a lifetime's safe passage, which they clearly couldn't, it seemed a lousy trick to play on a kid who never asked for the invitation in the first place.

She seemed to agree with that, but I could tell she expected something more. She would never have brought the subject up like that unless she'd given it a lot of thought. And once I started thinking about it, I couldn't get it off my mind, either.

Looking back, I realize how dumb I had been. When Rita talked about a child, she was really playing her very last card. It was the one card she figured might bind us tightly enough together that we'd have the courage to take the path that led to the painting, and the writing, and a way of life she'd never had. My mistake was in failing to read the signals. Even if I had, though, I still craved the exhilaration of doing that picture with her more intensely than anything else in the world.

In all the moves we made over the years, leaving that nifty river suite on the Thames was surely one of the saddest. There's something melancholy anyway when there's nothing but opened trunks all over the place, and you've got twice the gear to fill them. But when you're packing them to go back, instead of somewhere new, it's downright depressing.

With all the messages Rita was sending me at this time, I missed this one, too—her deciding she would like to take the boat back to New York, because she felt we'd had such a super-swell ride coming over.

She never even smiled when I said it wasn't the ship that interested her, but the chance to clobber me in my sleep again with the telephone receiver. Instead, she looked dead serious and said it was *always* dangerous to order martinis too early in the day. You'll remember that I'd been ordering a martini for that strange English girl when Rita had suddenly materialized, the prelude to the clobbering.

Anyway, she told me that was why she had bought me a watch, so that I would never, ever order another martini so early. I had never owned one before. She had bought it at Cartier's. It was the most beautiful watch I'd ever seen. What made it even more beautiful was that she'd saved the money for it out of the weekly check we got for our expenses. She explained all that as she was putting the watch on my wrist.

"You can see how well we can live, and still buy watches," she said. "But we don't *have* to live all this well, and we don't have to buy watches, do we?"

Somehow, I should have known what she was saying, but I guess I was feigning deafness. She was telling me that with her handling the money, we could live away from Los Angeles, away from the picture business—live as well as we *wanted* to and bring more meaning into our lives.

Anyway, that's how we went back. When we got to the Essex House in New York, she suggested that we cancel our plane reservations and take the train instead. She thought it would give us a chance to collect ourselves, though I contended we'd already done that on the boat.

So she said it would also give her a chance to do some sketching, and maybe I might sharpen a pencil or two while we studied the route of the Overland Express, or whatever it is you study on those trips. Once we were aboard, though, there was no sketching, and no pencils got sharpened. About the only thing I can remember was that we seemed to talk less with each passing mile and hit the bar car a little earlier each day.

Maybe it was the drinking, but that trip was a perfect example of my missing yet another of her messages. It should have been obvious by now that she was reluctant to get back to our house, and even more loath to head for the location to do *They Came to Cordura*.

If there was any drive I hated, it was the one from Los Angeles to Las Vegas. Seeing nothing but sage brush and scraggly little towns along the way left us both depressed. We were most of a day getting to the site where the company had set up quarters in a motel well outside Las Vegas. Since practically the whole picture had to be shot against a stark desert background, that dinky little town with its motel and surrounding barrenness looked just desolate enough.

Since we arrived on Sunday night, it wasn't surprising to find everyone with a drink in his hand. One of the first to greet us was

Gary Cooper. We had made *Vera Cruz* together, so it was as good as a reunion. But what made me feel especially pleased was to see how genuinely delighted he was at Rita's arrival. They'd known each other before, so I felt confident I'd be leaving her with at least one good friend.

The director was Robert Rossen, who had also done the script—and who was one of the best at his trade, which had a lot to do with Rita's ultimately deciding to do the picture. Once the greetings were over, she asked for the new script but was told Rossen was still working on it. I could see that disturbed her, because he had promised to have the rewrite finished before they started shooting.

We wandered over to his quarters, where he was holding court, drinking sundowners with all the others. He couldn't have been more warmly receptive, with a ready excuse for the delay on the script. But there's something about a picture company that reflects the style of the man at the helm, so I was already seeing omens all around me.

You can imagine how I hated to have to leave her, she looked so young and helpless and alone. But I had no choice. I had a script of my own, *The Unforgiven*, that I had to get ready, since our company had scheduled it as our next picture.

On the lonely drive back to Los Angeles, I had an empty feeling, as if I had somehow betrayed her. It wasn't just the guilt I knew I'd feel if the picture didn't turn out well, because she would never have done it if it hadn't been for my pressure. It was that no matter how hard I rationalized, telling myself the best thing for Rita was to be working again, I knew there was something much deeper troubling me. What I guess I didn't realize then was that in a marriage every separation is a little divorce. And we were in a business where it was intrinsically difficult to be together. So this was yet one more small divorce.

I was also preoccupied with the problem of raising money to launch our own venture. Thinking about that led me inevitably to Dorothy Dumont and her friend Biddy Lieding, the gilt-edged angel.

Now I'd banished Biddy from my mind before, because of Rita's uncanny ESP. So it wasn't until I was clean out of the state of Nevada, well into California, that I dared allow myself to begin thinking again along those lines. With every mile I felt better, because

I kept telling myself that getting this picture made was the key to our being together, the key to our future happiness. The more earnestly I told myself that, the more I believed it.

I don't know what I expected, not having seen Biddy since college, but I couldn't get over how much harder she'd become. She never smiled or laughed like she used to. My first shock was discovering her only interest was in making successful motion pictures. She also made it plain that if she was willing to gamble on me, then she didn't intend to gamble on *losing* me—she expected a lot more than me as partner for a single picture.

If I had any doubts about our meeting, Dorothy made it crystal clear after we left Biddy's place. How warm that palatial Bel-Air house of hers looked with all the lights blazing, and how cold it felt when we departed. Dorothy came right to the point; she told me if I expected any money, Biddy expected to marry me.

"What if I do all that and the picture still turns out to be a dud," I said.

"Then she'll be in the market for a new husband," Dorothy said.

It was hard to believe that the golden girl of my college days, Biddy Lieding, the gentle girl who'd inspired my first poem, could be that cynical and blasé.

"I just don't get it," I said. "Has she been married before?"

"Three times," Dorothy said.

That shook me. "Are you trying to tell me that Biddy has already made three lousy pictures?"

Dorothy burst out laughing. "You kill me," she said. "You really do."

When I thought the whole thing over, I realized there was more than one way to get what I wanted from Biddy, and not on her terms. So I let things ride while I devoted my energies to the script of *The Unforgiven*.

Curiously, it was a phone call from Clifford Odets, who told me he'd become a gourmet cook in the grand French tradition, that signaled a new optimism about things coming out my way. We had dinner at his house, just the two of us, with Cliff as chef. Never have

I tasted so many sauces. There was a sauce on everything but the wine in our glasses, and they all tasted more or less the same—suspiciously like the overflow from one of those Salvation Army soup kitchens.

Cliff was beaming away as if he were Escoffier, so I told him how great everything was. I've found it never pays to be really honest until you know what the other party is after.

The occasion for the dinner turned out to be his completing an original screenplay which he had written with Rita in mind. That very day he had made a production deal with 20th-Century Fox.

Naturally, I was hooked; in my book there was no finer living dramatist than Clifford Odets. So when he got through telling me the plot of his original, I could barely contain my excitement. I could see it was contagious, too, because before you could say Cordon Bleu, Cliff was telling me the secret of his gourmet cuisine.

It all began with his black housekeeper. Odets had been about to fire her because he'd caught her stealing his caviar, and pâté, and other assorted luxury items. Since Odets had a reputation as a great liberal, the housekeeper was appalled.

"It is hard to believe, Mr. Odets," she had told him reproachfully, bursting into tears, "that you is the man who wrote *Waiting for Lefty*.

Cliff said he was so disconcerted by what she said that he relented, and the relieved housekeeper reciprocated by giving him the secret of her culinary success—a slim book of recipes put out by the Campbell Soup Company. The entire trick to becoming a gourmet cook, she explained, lay in learning how to operate a can opener. To achieve the French touch, you combined two soups, and to move into the Escoffier class, you blended *three*.

I pretended to be overcome by his letting me in on such a valuable secret, as it gave me the opening to let Cliff in on a far more important one of my own—the secret of Rita's comic genius. When I told him about her dance routines, and the repertoire of characters she had created, he couldn't have been more enthusiastic. I managed to convince him that the plot of the original he'd just sold to Fox sounded as if it could easily be turned into an outrageous comedy.

If it had been a man with a lesser talent, he might have taken exception to such a suggestion. Not Clifford Odets. That's what set him apart. As he said, comedy was a challenge he had thought about, but never taken.

Since the male lead in his piece was a macho cop who discovers he is going deaf, which accounts for his sadism toward his wife and partners, we both began thinking in terms of Jack Lemmon, rather than Marlon Brando. After a few more working sessions marred only by Cliff's insistence on preceding each one with another Campbell soup gourmet spectacular, we knew we were on the right road. Then when I introduced 100-proof martinis before Cliff donned his chef's hat, we knew we had it licked. So it was right about then that I decided to head for Rita's location outside Las Vegas. I couldn't wait to tell her—I was that excited.

They were shooting a chase scene on horseback when I arrived on the *Cordura* location. It had to be 150 degrees out there in the desert. Except for the big tent where the company ate and the air-conditioned trailers for the stars, it was about as near to getting comfortable in a blast furnace as I'd ever been.

The horses were all lathered up when they came galloping out of a dry gulch in pursuit of Rita. I don't like to be forever bragging about her, but she rode a horse with the same grace she did everything else. The director, Robert Rossen, seemed to like what he saw, because the company broke while he went about setting up the next shot.

One of the niftiest things about Rita was the way her face would light up when she saw me. She could make me feel as though it was the luckiest thing in the world that *I*—of all people—should drop by out of the blue.

Characteristically, she looked as cool after all that riding in the heat and dust as if she had just stepped out of a cold shower. Only I could see immediately we weren't going to get a chance to talk, what with Coop wanting to run over his lines with her for an upcoming scene, then Van Heflin insisting that she readjust his toupee.

I really got a kick out of Van's confiding to me later that he surely didn't want me to think there was anything funny going on behind my back, simply that Rita had a feel for the rug atop his skull like no hairdresser he had ever met.

Just to put him at his ease, I told him it was from her working all these years with mine—a reckless mistake, because he proceeded to give my hair such a tug it brought tears to my eyes, and a sizable hank of hair came out. But it was worth it, because Van just stood there, shaking his head in admiration at finding it so secure.

I've always felt uncomfortable on anyone else's set, because I don't think it's right to intrude on people at their trade, even if it's your own wife. So I told Rita I'd meet her back at the motel. As I was leaving, she slipped her copy of the script into my hands.

"This is Bob's rewrite," she said. "I wish you'd look at it."

By the time she and the rest of the company returned to the motel I had read the script. So while she showered, I wandered over to Rossen's quarters. There's a loneliness to any location. I've seen the most talented of men fall apart at the seams when they leave their wives and the security of their homes. So drinking was a natural part of on-location living. But when it began to get out of hand, it was the handwriting on the wall.

As soon as I saw how glad Rossen was to see me, I wished I hadn't come.

"Did you read the script?" he asked, after I'd had a quick drink and started to go.

"No, I meant to, but I didn't get a chance," I lied. "I just wanted to say hello."

"Well, don't read it," he said, "it's no improvement." He looked bleak as he replenished his drink. "I don't know why, but I can't seem to get with it."

That was what I told Rita, when I got back to her. Just that single, sad line that said everything. We both felt for him, because he was a good man, and talented. What he was saying, without really coming out with it, was that *Cordura* was going to wind up as just another picture.

Even though I knew Rita had been saying this to herself, Rossen's admission had an impact on her. It wasn't the twelve-week grind in these roughest of circumstances—I knew her well enough to know that—but the three months gone from her life, and no way ever to get them back.

To distract her, I told her about Clifford Odets and the fabulous comedy he was doing for her. I told her how he was tailoring the male lead for Jack Lemmon. I couldn't stop talking—I was that carried away—which probably explains why it took me longer than usual to realize Rita had hardly reacted at all.

Then, in her quiet way, implying that she had strong convictions in this area, she said she had no intention of working after *Cordura*. She just wanted to read all the things she had never read and, when she wasn't doing that, she wanted to paint. And she wanted to do all this somewhere we had never lived before.

Not only did I have to bring her around with some fancy maneuvering, but I had to make sure that when I did, she wouldn't be able to say later that she didn't remember ever agreeing to such things. I had found the more we were drinking lately, the more she somehow forgot—especially the things I found extra important.

So I resorted to my old ruse, drinking most of each of her drinks, but I was cautious about pacing myself this time. The debacle of that secret film footage was not forgotten.

Ultimately, we agreed to agree. After she finished *Cordura*, I had to do *The Unforgiven* in Mexico, which was to star Burt and Audrey Hepburn. So she could spend that time down there doing nothing but reading and painting. Then we'd visit Cuba, since neither of us had ever been there.

I didn't tell her Carol Reed would be shooting *Our Man in Havana* down there at the same time. I wanted to surprise her later, knowing how much she liked Carol. Also, I was hoping he might be the key to getting her to do the Odets script.

I simply said that as far as Clifford was concerned, I would tell him she would do the picture. After getting his hopes up, I felt obliged to give him that much. Then later, if she decided not to do it, he could still console himself with the knowledge of how much she'd wanted to in the first place. And as a special friend, he would never hold her to a commitment.

Well, with that final reservation, she agreed to all the rest. What I couldn't get over was the way I was drinking all her drinks but never feeling really drunk. But what I didn't know until much later was that she was drinking most of mine. It was like a bad O. Henry story: She was worried that *I* was drinking too much, and vice versa.

After my return to Los Angeles, another three weeks remained until she was finished with *Cordura*. That meant she had all that additional time on that deadly location, knowing she had to give her best but without any reward. I knew she would come back a wreck, and I was right.

In anticipation, I had booked us out on an evening flight for Mexico the very day she got back. She was in a state of emotional exhaustion, but my instinct was good—she welcomed the idea of a brand-new scene in a brand-new country.

If there was a tense moment, it was when I insisted on dropping by to see Odets. After all, she was the reason for everything he was doing, so I knew how much her visit would mean to him.

Cliff was too caught up in his writing to notice how quiet she was. He started reminiscing about *The Sweet Smell of Success*, a picture we'd done together. Whenever we'd get stuck on the story line, I'd start imagining the picture with Groucho Marx in Burt's role. Magically, it would get Clifford laughing, and before you knew it, we'd have come up with a solution.

We got so carried away we had forgotten Rita, when she suddenly got to her feet. She would feel a whole lot better about her part, she said, if Clifford was writing it so that *Groucho* could play it, in case she didn't measure up. That was her way of telling me she still hadn't committed herself. I knew she could do Groucho as well as Groucho. So it surprised me no end, knowing how tired she was, when she did an imitation. It was a brand-new routine I had never seen her do. I thought Cliff was going to split, he was that excited.

I had no idea what had provoked her Groucho imitation, although I let myself believe it was because she was secretly hooked on the project but didn't want me to know it.

One thing for sure, we couldn't have left Cliff in a better mood. Then Rita decided we should drop by and see my folks. I tried to make her understand we didn't have that kind of time. But she was adamant—if we had time for Clifford, then we'd better make time for my folks. As soon as we arrived, Rita and the old man retired to the bar for a hooker. But this time, I could tell from the way my mother was studying me that it had been *her* idea.

"Isn't there any way you can slow everything down?" she asked.

"I feel fine."

"I wasn't thinking of you."

That's the trouble with mothers. They think because they gave birth to you, they automatically know more than you about the person you married. How could I ever make her understand the emotional significance of Rita's restlessness—of her need to be a gypsy?

So once Rita and the old man had their hooker, I made the perfect excuse to get us out of there. I said it was important for Rita to get a snooze before our takeoff. As we were leaving, Rita insisted they join us in Durango. She'd been insisting that on every trip we had taken, starting with London, so it came as a surprise when my mother said, "Maybe we'll just take you up on that."

Everything began to come apart for me in Durango when Audrey Hepburn fell off an Arab stallion she should never have been riding in the first place. It happened during the shooting of a scene for *The Unforgiven*. Instead of using a double, she'd been conned into doing the scene herself.

Everything had been moving along so beautifully, too. We figured we had the perfect chemistry when we managed to get Audrey to play opposite Burt, and we had been right. It was inevitable that, having to shut down while she recuperated, we would lose our precious head of steam.

So instead of getting out while everyone was still talking to each other—a rare enough occasion in the homestretch on *any* picture— we had to stick around and breathe sand for another week or two.

I could begin to see a change in Rita. Up until then she seemed content playing golf on the crummy course where the only grass was on the greens, and not too much of it there, while the fairways were nothing but sand.

Since we intended visiting Cuba as soon as the picture was done, she had been studying everything she could find on the country—not just the geography but the people, as well as the turmoil that was being stirred up by a revolutionary named Fidel Castro.

It was another special quality of Rita's that I was always going to adopt in my own life, but never did. When she went somewhere new, she not only made a point of steeping herself in its traditions

and geography, but its language as well. Along with her painting—
the way she started each day—she also had the job of running the
house. Since we had a covey of servants who came with it and none
of them spoke English, she was rapidly improving her Spanish.

Anyway, into this darkening atmosphere rode my parents. In all
my years in the picture business, that was the first and only time they
showed up on location. They had driven down with another couple.
According to my father, it was the other couple who'd talked them
into joining them for a tour of Mexico. Knowing my parents, I should
have been wary.

Rita was transformed, she was that delighted to see them. She
insisted they all stay with us, taking them in hand like some kind of
tour guide.

We were on a collision course. While Rita was more at peace with
life than I had ever seen her, I was sinking into depression. I knew it
was more than the shutdown. I was desperate to get on to Cuba and
into a discussion of the Odets script with Carol Reed.

I became aware of how much it had gotten to me one evening when
Rita and my mother arrived over an hour late for dinner. I was
irritated more than concerned.

My mother smiled her most patient smile. "After we've had a
drink, I'll explain," she said. "I don't know why you didn't go on into
dinner." That only made me more irritated.

"Because we were worried," I said. "We didn't know where you
were, and you're over an hour late."

Rita looked up from fixing their drinks and, not too friendly,
either, said, "You'd better tell him where we've been. We wouldn't
want him worried."

My mother took her drink from Rita. She had a leisurely sip,
studying me all the while. "We've been to church. Rita decided on
the visit, in order to pave the way for yours."

"Mine?" I exclaimed. "Why me?"

"We figured it's your last chance to be saved."

"Saved?" I said. "Saved from what?"

"Yourself," Rita said.

She was wearing a smug, self-satisfied look. I had sworn I wouldn't
let this sort of needling get to me, but I was on the verge of blowing.

My old man must have sensed it, because he broke the mood. He started laughing. "It's too late. You're too late," he looked at my mother. "You better tell them, Jim. Tell them about the church basketball championship."

In junior high school, I had played in a church basketball league. In the championship finals, we were beaten by the Methodists. My father never went to church, I explained, but my mother did. And since she was a Catholic, I had been baptized Catholic, too. So the next year, when I came home from playing in the finals again, my father asked who won.

"Just like last year," I told him. "The Methodists beat us again."

"How does it look for next year?"

"We'll have the same team, they'll have the same team. Same outcome, I guess."

I was on my way out of the room, when my father said, "Ever think of becoming a Methodist?"

Well, that sure slowed me up. When I turned back to him, I saw his eyes glinting wickedly. "Just *don't* tell your mother," he said.

My father started laughing all over again at that, so I went on to tell how the next year I became a Methodist and we won the championship and I got my first gold basketball. That was when I noticed my father's laughter petering out. And then I saw why—my mother was giving him the evil eye.

Later, in our bedroom, I was telling Rita how close I had come to making a fool of myself, but what a nifty thing my father had done, stepping in like he did.

Rita just gazed off with that faraway look of hers. "I wonder if you know how lucky you are," she said, "to have your mother."

"Oh," I said, confusedly. "Well, she didn't seem to take too kindly, after all these years, to learning about my losing my religion."

"She already told me the story."

That really surprised me. "She did?"

"She was just humoring your father when she pretended to be hearing it for the first time."

"Then my mother made that up, about stopping by the church?"

"Of course," Rita said patiently. "We went by the set, and when you weren't there, we had a couple of drinks with Audrey's husband."

"Oh," I said. I felt I had to say something nifty about my mother after the cool way Rita told me that, because I didn't want her to think I favored my father, but I really couldn't think of anything special my mother did, except to play a mean game of bridge once every week in the afternoon.

"What if you discovered," Rita said, "that your mother never played bridge at all on those afternoons, but had a lover instead?"

She nearly made me bust a gut, I got to laughing that hard at the ridiculousness of such a notion. But when I saw her frowning, I eased up.

"If you *had* made such a discovery," Rita said, "I guarantee there'd have been no laughter. Not from you, or your father, or your brother. Because those three male egos of yours would have collapsed like three pricked balloons."

Now I'd have died before I'd let Rita know, but she was absolutely right. Just her mention of an affair—just the *word* coming from her lips—made me begin to worry about such a thing actually happening with her if I didn't pay more attention to her. The very thought was appalling to me—the thought of her taking that tremendous talent of hers and handing it over to someone else. Strange as it may sound, that very concern was to become an obsession.

Nobody should welcome a robber, but I did because it drove such paranoid thinking out of my mind for the time being. It was several nights later. We were sleeping—at least I was—when Rita heard strange noises in the hall.

I got up and made sure our bedroom door was locked, then I took a big drink of vodka, which I kept in a carafe on the night table, since no one drinks the water in Mexico. I was all set to go back to sleep, when she said I had to do more than that. After all, my parents were in the house. Knowing my old man, I was sure that if he'd heard the same noises, he'd be drinking vodka, too, so I wasn't really worried. But just to make Rita feel better, I suggested calling the police. Luckily, her Spanish was good, because in no time at all the police showed up.

Well, everything had been stripped from the upstairs two floors, except from the bedrooms where people were sleeping. Even the grand piano was gone. Amazing that we hadn't heard the sound of a getaway car or a truck.

The chief of police was right out of one of those old Warner Brothers mystery films. He and his troops quickly rounded up everyone in the basement, including all the servants and, astonishingly, everything that had been stolen—even the grand piano. There must have been twenty-two people living in one room underneath that house. That's how poor the natives of Durango were. What possessed them to rob everything upstairs and put it all downstairs, and think they'd get away with it, I couldn't imagine. But Rita insisted on blaming herself for having tipped the chief off to the fact that there had been no getaway car.

She was really upset. The poverty of those people haunted her. What was worse, she cut off all the liquor, including my bedside carafe. She felt strongly, which she made very plain, that it was wrong for us to be drinking champagne and expensive Irish whiskey and vodka, when the poor people of Durango were homeless and starving.

Naturally, my old man didn't waste any time in getting out of there. He told me before he left that Rita had the same problem as my mother.

"I don't know why," he said, "but when they get feeling sad, the first thing they cut out is the liquor. When the liquor is the only thing that can *keep* them from being sad."

While we had this moment alone, I asked him how they'd really come to make the trip in the first place?

"If it hadn't been for the Cooks, I doubt if we would," he said.

The Cooks were the couple they were traveling with. "That's what you said when you arrived."

"Yes, I did, didn't I?" Then he smiled. "Your mother was concerned. She felt you both looked on the ragged edge when we saw you last in Los Angeles."

"Rita had just finished a picture," I reminded him. "She's feeling great now."

"She looks it."

"So do I."

"Maybe you should make this your home. It might not hurt to stay on for a stretch and continue to do the things Rita likes to do." I nodded. "Think about it. You wouldn't have to do it year round."

If I'd really thought about it, I'd have seen how right he was. Rita had evolved a full day every day for herself. A rewarding day. But it never entered my mind that anyone could be content in such an out-of-the-way place.

Once my folks were gone, Rita became a sort of local Florence Nightingale. We were lucky to have air fare left. Of those people who had been arrested, there wasn't anybody she visited who didn't need a handout. It wasn't until we flew out of there for Havana that I felt we had our future back on the track again.

Havana was a stark contrast to the poverty and despair of Durango. Not that the city didn't have its *barrio*. But it was the last year of the Batista regime, and the place was wide open, flourishing with night life and casino gambling.

Sir Carol Reed's production company had made our reservations. When word got out that Rita Hayworth was coming down, the hotels outdid themselves in bidding for her presence. None of them were interested in remuneration—they merely wanted the cachet of being able to say she had stayed at their hotel.

So we settled on the hotel where Carol was staying, and wound up with what was referred to as the presidential suite. It was as if we had walked into a greenhouse—I've never seen so many tropical plants and gaudy hothouse flowers. And that was just the beginning. Wherever we turned, there was candy and fruit and nuts and cigarettes, not to mention a paneled gameroom with a fabulous bar and an antique pool table.

After having to sneak all my drinks those last days in Durango, because of Rita's personal prohibition, a pitcher of martinis was my first priority the moment I heard her shower running. Carol and I both agreed that ice-cold martinis were as crucial to a reunion as having wives who put up with us. We always waxed sentimental about our wives after four or five martinis. . . .

Anyway, after that first wonderful shudder, I launched into an account of the birth of Odets's comedy. And when Carol said he would be interested in directing it if the script turned out as well as it sounded, it was the first time my dream of seeing Rita star in a comedy role—and in our own production—seemed likely to be realized. With Sir Carol Reed's name linked to the package, I couldn't see how we could miss getting the financing. If Rita felt half as enthusiastic about Carol as I did, then I had truly found the key in him. Although she and I hadn't had time to discuss it, I still felt like we should celebrate. And Carol loved any reasonable excuse for celebration.

So we started out by touring the town. I couldn't get over the lavishness of the casinos. And the food! Especially *feijoada*, that fabulous black bean dish with rice and onions. I took to *feijoada* like I did to my first martini—had it even for breakfast, and once from room service at midnight.

It was also that same evening when Carol played one of his practical jokes while we were shooting dice at the crap table in a plush private club where the old money of Havana—including Batista himself—always gathered. With fascists blowing expensive cigar smoke all over the place, Carol didn't even lower his voice when he told us that one of Castro's trusted lieutenants had told him Fidel had expressed a desire to come to the set and meet Rita.

Now you must remember that at this time Fidel Castro was thought of not so much as a threat to the Batista dictatorship, but as just another troublesome revolutionary somewhere up in the hills with a ragtag army.

Naturally, a rather large gap appeared in the conversation. And Rita played right along with Carol. She said her one desire, in giving Fidel Castro an autograph, would be that he would remember so that she might be spared when he and his executioners descended on the city. Well, the atmosphere in that club was certainly a good deal chillier when we left. Once safely back in our limousine, I had to ask if Carol really thought Fidel Castro might come down out of the hills.

Carol looked at Rita and chuckled. "Did you believe it, when I said that?" he asked her.

"No, not when you said he was doing it to get my autograph," she smiled. "No, I didn't."

"But Batista did, didn't he?" he said. Then he really laughed. "I just made it up. They all looked so bloody complacent I couldn't stand it."

I'd forgotten all about that evening, because once I told Rita of Carol's interest in directing the Odets script, she immediately forgot all her fears about doing such a picture. There was no way I could have felt more excited. In the days that followed, we made our plans for getting together on the script with Odets. Then we had to determine the best time to shoot the picture, and by the time we had all that figured, too, it was suddenly our last day.

We drove out to the suburb of Havana where Carol was shooting to say our goodbyes. He was in the midst of directing a scene when I noticed a young man approach Rita. There was something familiar about him, but when I couldn't place him I went back to watching Carol. It took several more takes before he was satisfied, and then it hit me. The young man who had come up to Rita was Fidel Castro. I turned, only to see him walking away. In the next moment, he had gotten into a car with a driver and was gone.

"My God!" I exclaimed to Carol. "She's been talking to Fidel Castro and never knew it!"

I couldn't have been further from the truth. I raced over to her with Carol and started asking if she had any idea to whom she had been giving an autograph, when I became aware her face was flushed crimson. Before I ever got out Fidel Castro's name, I knew she knew.

Right away, she told me how intently he had listened, and her implication was clear—listening was something I never did. That, she maintained, was why she knew Fidel would go on to greatness. Not one mention that he had risked his neck at being recognized. Imagine, doing anything so daring as to come down out of the hills —and just to meet her! But none of that had even registered. She told us that even before she was aware of what she was saying, she had blurted out everything that had troubled her in Mexico—the poverty, the illiteracy, the hopelessness. And Fidel had responded that poverty and illiteracy were the first two things he was going to remedy in Cuba.

So Rita asked him, once he took care of Cuba, couldn't he do something about Mexico? And he said he was sure those reforms would rub off on neighboring countries, just like they do on people who live in the same block.

"And then he thanked me," Rita said, as radiant as I'd seen her in many a day. "I can't tell you how much better it made me feel!"

Carol was clearly impressed. And so was I. "I told you, you could change the world." I was only half teasing.

"Yes, you did, didn't you?"

"They're all waiting to see you," I said. "Churchill, De Gaulle, Willy Brandt . . ."

"Then let's get on with it," she said and linked her arms in ours, and we started off, as though we were going to turn the world around right then.

"Hey, hey," I laughed. "We've got to make our picture first."

Well, that slowed her down some. "At least we can have a drink, now the ban's off," she said, smiling again. "And since he's responsible, we've got to have a farewell toast to Fidel." So we went to Hemingway's favorite bar and saluted Fidel Castro.

It had been a long stretch away. Except for a few hours, Rita hadn't really been back at our house for nearly five months. There had been the *Cordura* shooting, then my picture in Durango, and finally our meetings with Carol over the Odets script in Havana.

So I saw our reunion with Clifford as heralding a whole new era. It had never entered my mind to do more about keeping in touch with him than to drop him an occasional amusing card or note, signing both our names.

That's why, when Rita and I rode over to his house that first day back and I heard his poolside stereo speakers blasting out Wagner, I had a dread sinking sensation.

"There hasn't been a death in the family, has there?" Rita asked.

If I'd had any lingering doubts about Clifford, they were dispelled as soon as we saw him. He looked suicidal. If I'd had my way, I'd have gotten out of there, and fast. And I wouldn't have returned until he was playing Guy Lombardo, because I could see nothing but compassion written all over Rita's face.

Cliff had a big scarf wrapped around his shoulders that made him look like an aging pawnbroker down on his luck. Somberly, he announced that he had just gotten out of jail. It sounded as if he was referring to solitary in Alcatraz. Why, I ventured to ask, had he been arrested? He could hardly wait to unravel his tragic story.

In our absence, he had had a sense of potential treachery in his household. He said he couldn't be more specific, but he knew someone had an underlying hatred for him. It was an endless succession of *little* things—flat tires on his car or broken points on his pencils when he sat down to write.

Since his wife had died, he had lived in a big house on Roxbury Drive in Beverly Hills with the housekeeper I've already mentioned, his father, his two young children, and an uncle.

To verify his suspicions he did something only the greatest living playwright would be clever enough to think of doing, he enlisted the aid of a handwriting expert. Without any of the household knowing, he had samples of their handwriting analyzed. It came as no surprise that the expert was a woman, and damned attractive at that. And without ever having analyzed Clifford's handwriting, she *knew* he was right for her. Matrimonially, I mean. Clifford happened to be a very good-looking gent whom women were always trying to marry, feeling he needed a mother for his children. If you knew Cliff, though, he mainly needed one for himself.

Anyway, the lady expert discovered it wasn't the uncle who kept using Clifford's toothbrush behind his back, or the housekeeper who stole the caviar, or either of his children, who were always using the telephone when he tried to call home from his office.

That left only his father. According to the expert, his handwriting showed an underlying hostility toward Clifford. And where he had never noticed it before, Clifford now saw a shiftiness in his father's eyes whenever they were together. So Clifford recognized what he had to do for the morale of the household and he did it. He threw his father out.

It was the single most traumatic experience of his life, Clifford said. Up until then, he had always thought his father liked him. So after he did the deed, he had a few tequilas and limes. And salt, of course. Then he drove to the liquor store for some more tequila and bought some more limes. On the way back he got arrested for drunk driving. But instead of Alcatraz and solitary, he had spent one night in the Beverly Hills jail.

Cliff paused dramatically, while Rita and I exchanged wondering glances. We couldn't quite believe that this was the whole story. You don't go into terminal depression when you've been lucky enough to find an excuse to toss your old man out after he's been enjoying your hospitality for a dozen years.

Well, Rita blew her nose. I knew she was catching a cold, but Cliff immediately misinterpreted it as her terrible sadness for him.

That was when the first tear rolled down his cheek. Then another, and another. Then the deluge. And that was when Rita started crying, too.

I don't know why I didn't join in, because I had to be feeling worst of all. I saw everything slipping suddenly away.

Clifford sank onto the sofa next to Rita, and her perfume, or something, seemed to help him get a grip on himself.

"I'll never be funny again," he sighed. "Not in this lifetime."

There it was. Somehow, I had to get a finger in the dike before their tears washed our whole future away.

"Let's just take it one day at a time, Cliff, old boy," I said. If there was ever a phrase I hated, it was that one, but it was the best I could manage in the circumstances.

"I can't do the comedy, even though I promised I would," Clifford said. "I'm going to have to go back to the way I originally wrote it."

Rita was blowing her nose again. "We understand."

It killed me, the way it suddenly became we.

"No reason to rush these decisions, Cliffie." I gave it one more try. "You and Rita have a lot at stake here, so I'd suggest we just take it one day at a time."

"You're free to leave the project, Rita," Clifford was saying, and you can see again how important I was to the conversation. "I want you to know that."

Rita sighed, which always got to me, even when I wanted to murder her. "I wouldn't think of it," she said.

"The old ship may be doomed," Clifford said.

"Then we'll go down together."

With each banal line of dialogue it was getting worse. Bad enough that Clifford had given up turning the project into a comedy. But for Rita to commit herself to something that could do nothing to further her career was madness.

In the days that followed, the more I argued for her to walk away from the Odets project, the more adamant she became. It was more than having made a commitment, and honoring it. Odets had told her he had no intention of holding her to it. I couldn't help feeling that she had met a kindred soul in Clifford. In his way, he was just as lost as Rita.

In my heart I really admired Rita for sticking with him. Especially since Clifford was directing his own script, something he had only done once before. Naturally, I would have given anything for the picture to be great, but that wasn't to be. An original talent like Clifford's should never be exposed to production-line pressures. In this instance, he was working for a big studio that insisted on having a say, which meant he was inevitably inhibited.

In the end, the people who suffered were the performers. Just as it did in *Cordura*, a picture reflected the man at the helm. When he got shaky or uncertain, there was no way to keep the crew confident or the ship on course. It might have been easier for Rita if *The Story on Page One* had been made on location, but it was shot at the Fox Studios in Los Angeles. I could see the tension building in her—that old sense of claustrophobia—of everything closing in on her.

Ironically, I had just read the galleys of a wild, crazy, funny novel set in Greece. After all my searching, I had finally found the perfect vehicle for her. I was determined to get the money to buy the property, even if we had to put the house in hock, then I planned to direct it. I had no intention of gambling on anyone else this time around.

I had put the galleys into Rita's hands. It was a sunny Sunday afternoon. She was sitting on the shaded patio overlooking the pool and I was pretending to read the *Times*. I couldn't help glancing over every few minutes. The galleys were in front of her, but she was oblivious to them. I watched her eyes slowly mist over. She was hearing the music of the carousel again. I had a profoundly melancholy feeling. I knew that this time, time was running out.

If her talent hadn't been so prodigious, I could have walked away. After all, she had lived up to her side of the bargain. She'd said she would do *Cordura* so that we could get the house, and she had. Then she had agreed to do one more picture, which was to be the comedy for me. So while Clifford hadn't brought that off, it was no fault of hers.

How could I let that talent go untapped? I simply couldn't. Then inspiration struck. My folks. There had been a growing bond between them and Rita—especially between Rita and my mother. If anyone could bring her around it would be them.

Since they had an anniversary coming up, I mentioned it—intentionally avoiding any reference to the galleys I'd asked her to read. Rita returned from her reverie. The idea of a festive dinner for them clearly delighted her.

She had another week of shooting to go on *The Story on Page One*, so she decided on the following Saturday night. In that way, she said, it could be a triple celebration.

"Triple?" I said.

She was beaming now. "Yes, triple," she emphasized. "First, we'll be celebrating your parents' anniversary. Second, the end of my picture. That's enough to make any evening."

"You said three."

"I know," she said. "I can't tell you what the third will be, because I don't know myself." Then she smiled, a warm smile, as if she was hoping it would help me understand. "My future."

The scene had been set. Now how was I to get Rita launched into some of her comic dance routines? She never did them unless she was a little giddy, and even then I had never seen her do them for anyone else except that night with the police. But I was convinced that once my folks were exposed to her incredible talents, they'd be the first to agree with me about her future.

We were sitting around after a nifty dinner, when Rita took out her castanets. It was as if she was reading my mind. No prompting or anything. She took them out and showed my mother how she put them on. Then she began making them come alive. She had already put on some of her favorite tapes for the evening; next thing, she was on her feet and had the folks spellbound with her dancing.

"You didn't forget, did you?" my mother asked, all smiles, when Rita paused. When we were in Mexico, my mother had told Rita how much I'd talked about her way with the castanets. So Rita had promised her that when we got back to Los Angeles, she would do the dance she'd done when my mother first saw her that time in Tijuana.

Naturally, my folks were too excited to settle for that, so Rita did some of her routines from various pictures. But it was when she started improvising—clowning them up as only she could—that my folks were carried away.

She wasn't being nearly as outrageously comic as when she was alone with me and had had a bit to drink. But it was enough to start my folks laughing and applauding so hard they couldn't stop, not even after she'd paused to catch her breath.

The moment for stating my case couldn't have been better. "I can't think of anything more wonderful than to have such a talent." My folks nodded and smiled their admiration. "Unless," I said and paused significantly, "it would be the thrill of sharing such a talent with the world."

"I'm afraid," Rita said quietly, "we're in an area where your son and I disagree."

"I can't understand why, either," I said. "If you're lucky enough to blessed with such God-given ability, then I feel you have an obligation to share it."

I never figured on opening a hornet's nest. I'd been that sure of my logic. But that was exactly what I'd done. And what was worse, not only did my mother disagree with me, my father backed her up. Just because a person had a rare talent, they argued, she didn't owe anything to the world or anyone in it.

"I can't believe anybody can be so blind," I said, trying not to raise my voice. "It's like being allowed to see a Renoir, only to discover he feels no obligation to show it to the world." I was just getting wound up, when my mother interrupted me.

"Wouldn't it be nice, as long as we're deciding her future, if we heard from *Rita?*"

When I turned to her, I could see Rita was deeply upset. Her eyes never wavered from my face. "People don't *mob* Renoir because of his paintings." She said this very quietly. "They admire him as an artist, not as a personality."

I knew she was referring to that night when we nearly lost our lives to the mob in Soho. Once that had registered, she got to her feet, then kissed each of my parents on the cheek.

"I wish I'd had the two of you in my corner at an earlier age."

That was all she said. It was also the end of the discussion. At least I thought it was. Since it was raining, I had planned to drive my folks home. While I was having a stirrup cup, my mother nailed me. She started out by reminding me that in my whole life she had never criticized me. Not from day one. And just to make sure I got the message, she elaborated; she began by ticking off things way back in my youth, like the time I set fire to the schoolhouse and nearly burned it down. I have to admit she seemed to have something for just about every year after that.

"Maybe we should send all this in to the *Guinness Book of Records*," I said.

She didn't even smile. For the first time, it hit me—she really did have something on her mind.

"If you want to destroy yourself, Jim, you have every right," she said. "But you *haven't* the right to destroy Rita, and that's what you're doing."

I was touched by her concern and, to make her feel better, I admitted that we'd been drinking too much, and that Rita was working too hard at making movies she hadn't liked in the first place, and living in a town she didn't like, either. But, I explained, it was really all a prelude to our dream in which Rita would play a major comedy role and I would direct her. It would be the fulfillment of *both* our careers.

"What you saw tonight wasn't even close to what she's capable of. Even she has no idea how great her talent is," I told her. "I've seen it, so I know. But because she has to drink a lot to get into it, the next day she never remembers what she's done."

My mother shook her head ever so slightly—as if she were seeing me for the first time and couldn't credit what she saw.

"You don't really *believe* she doesn't remember?" my mother said grimly.

"She told you she didn't?"

"She's never mentioned a word of any of this," my mother said.

I took a deep breath and tried to be patient. After all, how could she be expected to understand a person in a trade as foreign to her as acting. So I told her about how complex a person Rita was—and of the long shadow her relationship with her dominating, manipulative father had cast over her life.

In all my days, I've never heard my mother use as strong a word as damn, or hell. But she looked at me again, as if she didn't know me, and said, "I don't believe I've ever listened to such a crock of shit . . . ," she said, and broke off in exasperation.

I was speechless.

"Let me tell you something," my mother went on. "Rita does not forget. She just wishes *you* would."

My mother paused, to control her emotions. "You had a childhood. You woke up in the morning and you did what you wanted to do. When it came time to go to school, you still only went when you wanted to. And as you grew up, we even moved when you wanted. Once it was for a junior high school that had the best basketball and baseball teams. Then it was for a different high school that had the best tennis players . . ."

"Okay, okay," I said. "So what *does* she want?"

"She wants to wake up each morning and do what *she* wants to do. Not what the studio wants her to do. And not what some director wants her to do. And not what *you* want her to do. She wants the carefree youth you had—and that you *continue* to have—and that she's never had. She wants to paint—not that she expects to be a major painter, but she wants the freedom painting represents."

If I'd believed any part of what she was telling me—about Rita not really wanting to be a great comedienne—I know I'd have felt truly betrayed. But I didn't.

"I appreciate your concern, Mother, I honestly do. And I'm going to do something about it, starting right now. Because if I don't get back, there won't be any Rita to start doing it with."

I attempted a chuckle, which I figured would break the tension. My mother smiled. She had gotten it all off her chest, which hadn't been easy for her, and now she wanted me to know she would never bring it up again.

Driving home, I couldn't help but think about all my mother had said. The more I thought about it, the more I knew that she was well-intentioned but on the wrong track. True, when I'd first met Rita I'd had a lot of the same notions about her not having a girlhood and all. But once I discovered her true talent, I knew that was where her happiness must ultimately lie.

So I decided it was time to confront her—to ask her if she had any secrets I should know, and to give her, in return, the one I had been keeping from her.

She was still up, so I launched right into the story of my secret visit to Biddy Lieding to raise money. I could see how much she appreciated my honesty. I didn't delve deeply into it because I'd discovered early on that it was risky enough to introduce another woman's name into the conversation. When she didn't knock out any windows, or threaten me with the telephone receiver, I knew I was about to hear what I wanted to hear—her own secret.

My mother had been absolutely right. But to hear it from Rita's mouth was like hearing it for the first time. I was stunned.

"I really didn't drink so much I forgot what I did that night," she said. "I did all those crazy things because I wanted to make you laugh —that's *all* I cared about." I must have looked puzzled because she went on, as if she hadn't made herself clear. "I wasn't interested in anything *beyond* that."

In my whole life, I have never felt so let down. I guess the better word would be "betrayed."

In retrospect, I realize my old peripheral vision had failed me—I was no longer taking in the whole scene. In my mind, I was dealing with her image—with Gilda. So when I said I felt betrayed, that's who had betrayed me—Gilda, not the girl I had married. And with my vision as willfully blinkered as that, it was no wonder time was running out on me.

*   *   *

A curious thing about our town, there's no sense of change in seasons. It was one more aspect of the Holmby Hills Park that made it so special. The man who had owned and planned it had come from England. That was why the streets bordering it had names like Charing Cross Road, and the trees he had planted had been imported. So on this day, all the leaves were changing into scarlet and gold. It was probably the only place in Los Angeles where there was the feeling of fall.

The park had become our tranquilizer. I had picked it because I was uncertain about Rita's reaction to something I was about to propose. If there was an unpleasant problem to be faced, we seemed to summon a greater patience with each other when we confronted it there.

If we were to continue together, one of us was going to have to give in to the other. The last thing I wanted was for us to go through a divorce here, where my family lived. It would have hurt them terribly.

I had picked the park to tell her of a picture I could set up for us in Madrid—one requiring little effort from either of us. But it would provide the safety valve in case we split—it would get us out of Los Angeles, out of the country.

I expected a flat turndown, or at least an argument, since Rita had made it plain she had no intention of doing another film. But to show how quickly she grasped the situation, she didn't ask a single question. At any other time, she would have wanted to read a script. Then she would have wanted to know the rest of the cast, the director —everything down to the last detail—before she would consider committing herself.

Only this time she didn't. She knew intuitively why I'd brought it up. If she'd gotten sore or cross-examined me, I'd have felt better. I couldn't help feeling lousy for not having been more open.

She stood there under the flaming maple tree and looked at me for the longest time before she finally spoke.

"The last thing Clifford and I talked about was you," she said. "He told me you were the best he's worked with."

"There's no one I'd rather hear that from."

"I brought up the story of you and Harry Clork—about how you got your job working for him as a writer without ever putting a word on paper."

Her ability for remembering names and conversations never failed to amaze me. "What did Clifford say?"

"He said that you were kidding me."

"Maybe I was. I have this thing about writers and writing. So many refer to themselves as writers when there are so very, very few who can."

"How many have you actually known?"

"Two," I said. "Vincent Lawrence and Odets."

"Clifford thinks of you as a writer."

"No. He thinks of me as a sounding board, someone who stimulates him because I'm good at invention."

"He says there's no one better at construction."

"If Clifford says that, I believe him. But I wouldn't if he said he thinks of me as a writer."

Even then she'd touched me. At this late date, she was still trying to bring me around to her world of writing and painting. If it had been a less sensitive area, I would have been less blunt. But I wanted to make it plain to her once and for all: I hadn't been blessed with a talent for greatness. And if I couldn't compete with the Lawrences and the Odets, I didn't want to settle for less.

"You'll *never* know, if you've never really tried," she said.

"I know."

Those two words were as tough to say as any I've ever spoken. I was looking into those eyes of hers, and I could see the hope dying in them. Then she turned from me and dropped a couple of golf balls on the grass.

She moved one of the balls around with her club for a better lie, looked off at the green some seventy yards away, but didn't hit it. Instead, she turned back to me and her eyes were void of expression. She had used the moment to collect herself.

"If you think it's a good idea, then we should do it," she said.

For a moment I was bewildered. She was referring to the picture in Madrid. She didn't wait for my reaction, but turned immediately back to the golf balls.

I watched her hit them with that graceful rhythm of hers. I knew

I'd never find anyone else who could give a performance with such style, and still swing a club like that. She hadn't made one reference to money or salary. It was that unimportant in contrast to what she really wanted in this world. She truly had the mind of a man. I could think of no greater compliment.

No wonder my father loved to go off for a hooker with her. It made me smile, thinking about that. I began to feel better as I followed her to the green where she had hit the balls. She picked them up, then she began picking up these gloriously colored leaves.

"Why don't we grow old and become more beautiful like the leaves?" she said, as she watched them flutter back to the ground. "Do you realize, they're at their most attractive in their final days, when they're falling from the tree and dying?" That, she said, was how she wanted to grow old. She didn't want to look in the mirror one day and see the start of her first wrinkle, which would mean all her thoughts from then on would be melancholy ones, because she would begin to worry about the parts she was no longer getting.

"I want to look in the mirror and see the *excitement* in my eyes, not the wrinkles around them," she said. "But I'll never see anything else, unless I begin to look at the beauty all round me, like these leaves."

It was the nearest she came to direct confrontation. There was an edge of anger to her voice. But once she finished, she calmly went back to hitting golf balls. She had let me know in no uncertain terms that she had no intention of backing down, just because she had agreed to make this picture in Madrid. For such a slight and feminine person, she had pure steel running down her spine. If I still had any notion of changing her mind, I had my work cut out for me.

Among the plethora of errands we had to do on our last day in town, Rita included a visit to Adrian's. She still had that $5,000 credit there. I'd accompanied her on a number of shopping expeditions in New York when she had gone to Saks to replenish her wardrobe, and discovered I enjoyed it. The simpler the design, the greater its appeal for her. She had absolutely exquisite taste in clothes. She could take a suit or dress whose lines might appear severely masculine in the designer's sketch, and once she put it on, it somehow became extremely feminine.

She was never afflicted with indecision. Either she liked what she saw, or she didn't. Only that day at Adrian's, she liked everything—she never paused until she had spent the entire $5,000.

It wasn't that his clothes weren't beautiful, but they just didn't seem like Rita. Since she never turned to me for an opinion as she usually did, I'll admit I was miffed. Once we were in the car, I couldn't hide my irritation. "How in the world did you figure to get all those clothes made and altered, when we're leaving in the morning?"

She got that lovely, wicked gleam in her eye. "I thought you'd never ask," she said. "I didn't get them for myself. I got them for all those ladies who worked for us in Durango."

By tradition, we had our last dinner in town with my folks, and as usual, the evening was a delight. The full ritual was observed: The evening opened on Rita and the old man disappearing for their hooker, then my mother held sway on the piano for a stretch of ragtime, and finally we had one for the road.

What made it different, though, was that it was the first time in making our farewells that Rita hadn't insisted on their joining us on our trip. It wasn't that she forgot. I knew her better than that. She hadn't invited them because she wasn't sure we would still be together. For the first time, I began to feel the threat of divorce hanging in the air.

I couldn't shake it, even when the limousine picked us up the following morning. As we drove off, I found myself looking back, wondering if we'd ever live in that lovely house again.

In the past, a change of scenery had always brought a lift to our lives—especially for my gypsy, Rita. Only this time, it never happened. From the moment we left L.A.X., everything felt downbeat.

Madrid was no help, either. There was something bleak about the place that was reflected in the faces of the unsmiling people. Franco was still alive and running the government, so I guess it was no mystery why the citizens were plunged in gloom.

Never before had I had no interest in a picture I was making. And I knew the same held true for Rita. Not that she had ever in the past talked about parts she was playing, but in her quiet way she had always been very demanding of herself—determined to be letter-perfect during rehearsals before she would allow the director to start shooting. And the same meticulousness applied to her wardrobe, and everything else. This time, though, she was more like an automaton, simply going through the motions. She never ever got interested enough to call the director by his first name.

It's amazing how fast you become strangers, once divorce is in the air. I guess the most difficult aspect of any marriage, or any other relationship for that matter, is keeping the lines of communication open. But with someone as reserved as Rita to begin with, those lines were always tenuous at best. And I have to admit, I wasn't proving efficient at picking up the slack.

So many of the things that happened seemed to hold a mirror up to the past, which was no help at all. The film itself was a caper about stealing a painting from the Prado where we did a lot of our shooting. One day, who should arrive but a squad of nattily dressed military men, with swords in shiny scabbards and those helmets with plumes. Everyone in the Prado stopped at the sight of them, including our company, who were in the midst of shooting a sequence with Rita.

The detail came to a smart, military-type halt. One of them stepped forward and presented Rita with an envelope on a silver salver. He did a smart about-face, rejoined the ranks, and they all marched in cadence out of the museum.

Everyone was eager for Rita to open the envelope, so she did, right there. It was a splendiferous invitation to a ball at the palace honoring General Francisco Franco himself.

Shades of Havana! Here was a great chance for Rita to straighten Franco out, like she had Fidel Castro. Before we knew it everybody on the streets of Madrid would be smiling again.

In that moment I'd forgotten her feeling for the dying leaves in Holmby Park, and restructuring her life and all. In the excitement, I started talking about her still having time to take on Churchill, and

De Gaulle, and all those other heads of state who were anxious to see her—I was suddenly feeling that good again.

That's when I noticed the sad look in her eyes. She didn't have to say anything, because that look said it all. She was telling me in her way that that was the world—that make-believe world of ours—that she intended to put behind her.

The one person who did more than anyone else to ease the pain of those days was Rex Harrison, who played opposite Rita in the picture. Bad enough to be involved in a movie you had no feeling for—bad enough to have to pretend, because of the cast and the crew and everyone, that you were going all out to make it great. But to have your marriage unraveling at the same time—it really made having someone like Rex around a blessing.

At this time, Rex had a brand-new lady on his arm, who was to become his next wife. Rachel Roberts was Welsh, and I couldn't help but like her, because there was a lot of Rita in her.

I'll never forget one early Sunday morning, when Rex and I met to discuss some problems in the script. We ordered a bottle of Fernet Branca, just about the greatest alcoholic cure for alcoholism ever invented. Not only did it taste terrible, but it made it possible to see just one of each other, which should tell you why we chose it—and should also make clear how rough our previous night had been with our respective loved ones.

After we had downed that bottle, old Rex, who could look more rakish than any rake I had ever known, got his wonderfuly self-satisfied smile.

"James," I can hear old Rex say, "what would we do without them."

On this particular morning, that first bottle of Fernet Branca hadn't done its work for me, and the cobwebs remained. "I'll tell you what I would do, if I should find myself facing the world alone again," I said. "I'd make sure I *stayed* that way."

"A word of advice, if you don't mind, old boy," Rex said. "Wives are like gilt-edged stocks. The more you have, the greater your dividends."

"You mean it's a poor man who only has one wife?"

Rex shrugged. "Where would you go if Rita threw you out?"

I had to smile, in spite of the cobwebs, because I was remembering one particular shared limousine ride with Rex. With him were *three* of his ex-wives, who couldn't have been more congenial, because they shared a single concern: Rex's longevity. So all three were worrying about whether he'd packed his thermal underwear, whether he'd brought his umbrella and everything else that contributed to a long life.

Seeing my smile, Rex leaned across the table confidentially. "One further word," he said, "*always* leave them beholden."

While I hadn't taken that conversation seriously, I felt a chill when I contemplated a future without Rita. As hard as I rationalized— telling myself how much better off I'd be since she wasn't interested in my dreams of directing her—it wouldn't wash. I didn't even have an ex-wife to go to.

So along with the copious drinking, I found myself growing more anxious as the picture wound down. Times when I should have had fun, times that should have been memorable, just weren't because I knew Rita wasn't enjoying them.

Like a weekend with Juan Belmonte, who raised prize fighting bulls for the ring at his ranch outside Seville. Belmonte had revolutionized the art of bullfighting with a style that still prevails today. As old and infirm as he was, he was still a delight. He showed us why—even in his prime—he had been unable to flee from the bull. Instead, he had learned to work from a stationary position with the cape and make the bull come to him. Not that I'll ever forget that weekend, but I should have enjoyed such a rare opportunity far more.

Other moments come to mind, but the one that really stays with me and always will took place during our final week of shooting.

Rita had gotten up during the night and, not wanting to wake me by turning on a light, she had bumped her eye on the corner of the medicine cabinet. The next morning she had a slight shiner, which the makeup man was working hard to disguise.

"How'd it happen?" he asked.

"The black eye?" Rita said.

"Yes."

"My husband hit me," Rita said.

I knew they hadn't heard me come into the little room outside the makeup room, so I had picked up the script I'd left there and was on my way back out when I heard Rita tell that terrible lie.

"How can you stay married to a man who would hit you?" the makeup man asked.

"He can also make a room come alive," Rita replied, and there was no mistaking the pride in her voice.

Well, that single line catapulted me back to those early days when I was forever figuring out how I could hug her for things she said, or did. Here it was practically the last day of the picture—and me getting nerved up to walk away—and she says something like that. It was almost too much, if you know what I mean.

The last day of shooting finally did roll around, and we had the usual wrap party on the set. Then Rita, with that rare sense of humor that was forever lurking in those mysterious shadows of her mind, decided we should also celebrate the occasion privately by using the kitchen in our hotel suite. It would be a first, since in all the time we were there we'd never so much as boiled an egg. And she decided that we should each only invite one guest, and that I should do the cooking.

"Who are you inviting, or should that remain a surprise?" I asked.

She frowned, pondered a minute, then decided to tell me. "I don't want you to act smug or anything if he doesn't show up—because it's you."

My relief was overwhelming. Maybe it was because it could well be our last dinner together that made me realize why they always had such a fine spread for those fellows on death row—something to remember as long as you lived. So when she asked me who I was inviting, I could tell she already knew.

"You," I said.

"Well, all things considered," she said—and it was obviously what she was referring to—"I'm flattered."

Where she found the time, I don't know, but she'd bought a goose for me to stuff, and while I'd had some experience with Thanksgiving turkeys, this was another first. Naturally, we had each brought the other a present; she gave me a quart of Jack Daniels and I gave her a quart of Stolichnaya.

Just to get a feel for that kitchen, before making the acquaintance of the goose, we each downed a couple of straight ones from our respective gifts. In no time at all she was referring to me as Escoffier and I was calling her Charlie, after the one and only Chaplin.

It was while I was stuffing the goose that she was holding for me in the sink that she started reflecting. It was the first time, since she'd talked of the leaves in Holmby Park, that she'd allowed a word to creep into her conversation regarding our relationship.

She started by telling me how she'd had no intention of ever leaving Paris, until I came back into her life that time at the Ritz. And the only reason she did then, was because she remembered our discussion of our individual destinies when we first met at her house that long-ago Christmas Eve.

She said she just knew we could realize them both, because she felt we could do anything, if we did it together. Still, she said, the main thing she'd gotten out of our relationship—the thing that was far and away above everything else—was that for the first time in her life, she felt she could realize her dreams, if she had to, on her own.

While it was about the biggest compliment she could have paid me, she couldn't have put it more clearly on the line. That must have taken a lot of nerve, because she knew it could mean the end of the road for the two of us.

I really didn't know what to say, because I still couldn't see myself walking away from the plush life I so enjoyed—or *thought* I did—for such a fragile future. It wasn't that she wouldn't share her worldly goods, because I've already mentioned too many times that she was the most generous person I've ever met. But between us, we just never seemed to *have* any worldly goods.

Luckily, I didn't have to make my decision right then, because at that moment I ran out of stuffing. Neither of us could believe it possible. After all, I'd started out with over two quarts, which room service had said would be twice as much as we needed. But desperate for diversion, I pretended it would save time if I tore down to the kitchens myself.

Now I don't know how many more straight ones we had when I returned, but I brought back over three quarts of stuffing this time, and we were utterly mystified when we used all that up, too.

"My God, Charlie!" I remember exclaiming to her. "If that goose wasn't dead, I'd swear it was *eating* the stuffing."

Rita was so perplexed that she put on those half-moon spectacles of hers and peered at the goose. "Maybe it's *not* dead, Monsieur Escoffier," she said. "But shouldn't it be getting fatter, if it's eating all the stuffing?"

Since we didn't have any answers, we had another straight one. From the way she was studying me, I could tell she was determined *not* to be diverted.

"I want you to be very serious for a moment, because *I'm* going to be very serious," she said.

To play for time, I said, "There's no way I could take you seriously, unless you were wearing your serious hat."

The hat was one I'd picked out for her for the picture. She didn't particularly care for hats, but she looked super-elegant in this one. A little kooky, but elegant.

When she returned from the bedroom, she had the hat perched pertly on her head with her hair all tucked up under it. I still didn't have an answer for her, but I didn't need one.

"You know," she said, "it's your greatest talent that's destroying you."

I frowned at that. "You can't mean my talent for stuffing a goose."

"No, I mean your talent for using people," she said. "If you didn't have it, you'd be writing. But why bother to write, when it's so much easier for you to use the talents of others."

Those words hit home like nothing she'd ever said to me before. She had come up with her own solution—made my decision for me —unless I had something further to say. Unfortunately, I didn't.

That was the last thing I remember clearly about that evening, although we must have cooked the goose. Because there its skeleton lay on a plate beside the bed when I woke up.

The wall clock in the living room told me it was almost noon. I found her note on the mantel.

Have flown with Thelma to Majorca. Will phone you from there. Love, Rita.

Thelma was her English hairdresser. Rita had toyed with the idea of going to Majorca once the picture was over. It was a popular spot for unwinding under the sun. She knew I had to get on to Rome to finish the edit, so I wasn't too surprised she had gone without me.

I've never seen anyone who could indulge in a night of drinking like we had, then bounce up the next morning and take off. Rita *never* had a hangover. I was wondering at this, when I was struck by the biggest surprise of all. That note wasn't meant to explain her where-abouts. It was her goodbye. It was so obvious once I paused to think about it—so typical of Rita.

She'd gotten my answer last night, so she had left. If I had no intention of trying to make a career as a writer, then she had no intention of continuing as we were. She hadn't awakened me because she didn't want to risk an emotional scene.

Suddenly I had the worst hangover ever. Even the old Fernet Branca didn't help. I started wandering from room to room. If I'd had any lingering doubts, they vanished when I found she had taken all her things.

The only reminder of her was that nifty hat. It was in the kitchen perched atop the Jack Daniels bottle. Since there was one good jolt left, I paid tribute to that hat by downing it.

When I finished shaking, I knew that if I felt this bad, I had to live. I sank down onto a high-backed chair that had armrests and was just staring into space, when I noticed an odd-looking switch over the sink. I began to imagine that it turned on the juice for the electric chair I was occupying. I figured I had just left death row, so I'd be the first person in Sing Sing to have been executed by his own hand.

I honored by last request by placing that kooky but elegant hat of hers on my head. When the current finished me off, she'd know I went to my death with her on my mind.

I braced myself and threw the switch.

A terrible grinding began that told me it wasn't my day for dying, no matter how bad I felt. The sink began spewing up champagne corks, along with the five quarts of stuffing.

The mystery of the goose was solved. The reason it had taken five quarts was that Rita had been holding it over the garbage disposal. When the grinding reached a peak, so did the stuffing. Yosemite never produced a finer geyser. It was a tribute to Rita's ingenuity for having played one final practical joke. I didn't know whether to laugh or cry.

I couldn't believe my eyes—I blinked, but there she was, standing on the other side of the kitchen door. I don't remember turning the switch off, just walking out of the kitchen like a sleepwalker.

I still couldn't believe it was Rita. "I got your note," I said. "You were saying goodbye, weren't you?"

"Yes."

"I still can't believe you're standing here," I said. "What brought you back?"

"I forgot my hat."

"You didn't forget your hat."

She got that nifty look, which told me I had said exactly the right words, because she moved into my arms. She started trembling so hard I had to tighten my hold on her. A couple of times she tried to speak, but had to give up. There was no reason for explanations, anyway. It was all too obvious. Striking out on her own had been too much for her. So I knew there was no point in getting my hopes up, because nothing in her thinking had changed.

When she finally began to relax, I realized she was falling asleep in my arms. I eased her down onto the couch, although there was no need to worry about awakening her. Not after the long night she'd been through.

Once I'd covered her with a blanket, I sat down beside her. I wanted to be there when she opened her eyes, so she would know she wasn't alone.

I must have dozed off, because when I woke up, everything was spotless. That meant the maids had been in and out, completely unobtrusively. It was one of their trademarks.

That foolish, elegant hat of hers was still on my head. I took it off, then sat looking at it. I was thinking how it was the kooky side of her that I cared most about. But it was the elegant side she used to hide behind, when she wanted to shut out the world. Hopefully, I'd see the kooky side when she woke up. . . . Eventually she did.

In an effort to bring some lightness into the room, I gave the hat a place of honor on the mantel. As I did, I told Rita about turning on the switch in the kitchen only to have the stuffing erupt. I figured that had to provoke a smile, because that had been the very moment she walked in. So we drank a champagne toast to the hat, but as hard as she tried, I knew Rita was only smiling on the outside. I tried another toast. This time to our reunion. But that fell even flatter. We just sat drinking champagne as the atmosphere in the room grew grimmer.

Since we'd stopped opening the drapes, there was no way to tell night from day. I don't know why it became important, but I grew curious about the date. Had I wanted an easy answer, I could have picked up the phone, but since we'd ruled out contact with the world, that left the morning paper. We could see from the living room that several had piled up in the hallway.

I was about to take a look, when Rita spoke up. "What kind of a caveman are you?"

"Shouldn't a caveman know what day it is?"

"Not by looking at the newspaper," she said.

"Do you know what day it is?"

Rita got her real mysterious look. "Of course."

"No wonder the caveman carried a club and dragged his wife around by the hair," I said. "He just wanted to know what day it was."

"Even if she'd told him, he would have still carried a club and dragged her by the hair."

"He would?"

"Yes," she said, "because he knew he had an inferior mind."

The tension had stretched into such long periods of silence, even the champagne wasn't helping, so anything was a welcome diversion. I started to laugh, then Rita got to laughing, too.

If I'd been more aware, I would have made sure we took advantage of that single moment of comic relief. We would have opened those drapes, then we would have stepped out and faced the world.

We were back in our cave now, but with one monumental difference. Our original cave was used to keep the world out. This time, we were using it to keep us in, because we were that afraid of *going* out. So we didn't touch the drapes. Instead, we drank a toast to the brilliance of the female mind.

*   *   *

Double doors led into our suite. At the time of our arrival, we'd had extra locks and chains put on them until it looked as if we were guarding Fort Knox. We had to do that, because we never came back to the hotel without finding photographers or members of the press.

It was like coming out of a coma to hear the sound of banging on those doors, then to watch the police come crashing in. There must have been a half dozen of them. They fanned through the place led by an officer.

Since I didn't understand Spanish, I had to wait while the officer in charge talked to Rita. It seemed there had been the sound of a shot from inside our suite. The manager had used the phone to try and contact us, but when he got no answer, he had rung our bell. When he still couldn't raise anyone, he had called the *Guardia* and they had broken in.

While Rita was translating all of this, one of the police produced a handgun that had been recently fired. We must have looked foolish, because neither of us had seen the gun before. Yet it had been discovered right there lying beside the living-room sofa.

Then the officer held up that kooky, elegant hat. He pointed to a bullet hole in it. Then he turned to the straight-backed chair from the kitchen, which was now in the living room. The officer pointed out a bullet hole through the top rung.

Even I began to get the drift. If someone had been sitting in that chair with that hat on their head, they would have been a perfect target for a shot from the gun. It would have passed through the hat, then the chair, and finally, as the officer pointed out, embedded itself in the wall paneling.

As Rita translated, she was so overcome by the terrifying implication of his words, her voice trailed off. I put a steadying arm around her waist. I was worried she might faint. It buoyed her up sufficiently that she finished translating what the officer had said.

"He asked if I'd been sitting in the chair wearing the hat when the shot was fired. She slipped from my arm and sank onto the sofa. "I told him such a suggestion was laughable."

But nothing was laughable, because I had no recollection of anything. So maybe I *had* fired the gun. Only where it had come from, I hadn't the faintest idea.

I'd been watching one of the police pick up scraps of paper with writing scribbled on them. He handed the pieces to the officer, who puzzled over them, then turned to Rita.

She studied the writing, then the consummate actress took over. She slowly rose to her feet with all the elegance at her command. Once she started speaking, the officer's attitude began to change. Where he'd been officious, even haughty, now he became attentive. By the time Rita had put the scraps of paper into the pocket of her blouse, dismissing them in the same tone she was dismissing the officer, he had become totally subservient.

Everything was more than back to normal by the time the last of the police preceded the officer out. When I say more than normal, I mean that was when the officer turned back to Rita. I didn't need a translator, as I watched her produce a photograph of herself.

"For his granddaughter," she said to me, as she wrote her name.

All her bravado deserted her as soon as the officer left. She collapsed on the sofa, closing her eyes. This time, I thought for sure she had passed out. I poured her a brandy. She opened her eyes but didn't touch it.

"What did you tell them?" I asked.

It was an effort for her to speak, but she managed somehow. "I told them we were playing a game. I said we sometimes did foolish things when we finished a picture. It was our way of letting off steam."

"What was on the papers?"

"I don't know. I didn't have my glasses on, so I couldn't read. Right now, I don't want to know. I told them it was part of the silly game we were playing."

There were so many things I wanted to ask her, but I was afraid of frightening her even more. So I simply got a blanket and wrapped it round her. I kept wishing she would drink the brandy, but she continued to ignore it.

"What if one of us was wearing the hat when the shot went through it?" she said.

"Then it would have had to be me with the gun, like he said."

"No. *You* had the hat on when I came back," she said. "You could just as easily have had it on again, and *I* could have had the gun."

"They're gone," I said. "Let's forget it."

"I can't."

"At least for tonight."

She looked at me with such desperation it hurt. "You don't remember anything, do you?"

"No, but that's not the first time for me. Not when I've done as much drinking as I have these past few days."

"It is for me. It's the first time I really couldn't remember." She took a deep breath, then her whole body quivered with the sigh that followed. "I can't even remember where the gun came from, can you?"

"No."

As frightened and as frayed as she was, it was Rita who managed to get herself together. Not a lot, but enough to pull those drapes.

It was night outside. Neither of us cared. Not about that or what day it was. Our only concern was to get out of that hotel, out of Madrid, and on to Rome.

It was waking up, after going to bed in Rome, that we felt the fingers of normalcy beginning to take hold of our lives once again. It wasn't the rest, because neither of us slept. It was being awakened by a call from Thelma, Rita's hairdresser.

She was curious to know if we'd found a gun. She said she'd wrapped it in a towel, then slipped it into Rita's luggage, because she knew the immigration authorities never searched her things. Apparently, she'd forgotten that Majorca was a Spanish possession, so there would have been no customs for people from the mainland.

At that discovery we each realized we hadn't trusted the other. I mean, a gun just doesn't drop out of the blue like that one had.

I don't believe either of us realized how close to the naked edge we were. Our arrival in Rome had drawn an enormous crowd of jostling autograph fans and *papparazzi*. I had picked an out-of-the-way hotel, even booked the suite under assumed names. Yet the mobbing almost matched that night in Soho before we finally managed to escape to our rooms. So that call from Thelma may have been the most welcome call we ever received.

While I had to spend a couple of hours each morning in the cutting room, we spent the rest of our day trying to recollect the steps that had led up to the firing of that gun.

The biggest breakthrough came when we went over those scraps of paper. Each one contained a complaint against the other. The first I looked at was in her handwriting, speaking of my catering to her wishes by playing golf at Pebble Beach, and later at Saint Andrews —but only when I wanted her sufficiently indebted so that I could make my own demand upon her career. It hadn't hit her at the time, but she had become obsessed with the idea that I'd only married her to ensure her finishing *Separate Tables*, a picture she knew I considered vital to the new image we were creating for her.

In my case, the criticisms stemmed from her allowing me to believe she had no recollection of those fabulous routines she did when we were drinking. This had culminated in my paranoid conviction that someone else would be the benefactor of her rare comic gift if I agreed to let her walk out of my life to paint.

Once we got into all this—and we were doing it without one drop of liquor—I began to remember the cloudy, champagne-induced thinking that provoked it.

It was a macabre parlor game. Each of us was to write down our complaints about the other. The one who had the greatest grievance would get the first shot. We would put one bullet in the gun, then spin the barrel. It was to be an injustice collector's version of Russian roulette.

We realized that each of us could have taken a dozen shots at the other before the bullet was actually fired. Or perhaps there was only one single shot—fortunately, that one had brought the police.

We didn't allow ourselves to dwell on what might have happened. Instead, for the first time in our relationship, we had made a clean breast of everything we felt about each other.

Another week went by. It may well have been the greatest week we ever spent together. When I wasn't editing the picture, we used the time just wandering Rome's outlying neighborhoods, or visiting the galleries, but mostly talking now that we had opened the flood-gates.

The only reference to that night in Madrid was made by Rita the evening before she left. "Do you think we're sick?"

"Do you?"

"Yes," she said, "but just one of us."

I could see she was getting that look—the look that hid one of her rare smiles. We'd finished dinner and were drinking espresso in a restaurant under the trees. There was even a creek running past our table.

"Which one?" I asked.

"Whoever took the shot," she said. "You've *got* to be sick to miss at that distance."

"Then we'll never know?"

"I will."

"You will?" I said, surprised. "How?"

"The one who shoots that badly will be the one who hasn't the courage to walk away," she said.

I'd been fighting a smile of my own, but now I didn't feel like smiling anymore. "You're leaving."

"In the morning." When I remained silent, she said, "You're not coming."

"No."

I tried to talk her out of it. The one new and convincing argument I had was that we'd finally gotten to know each other. But it was to no avail.

"If I stay, we'll destroy each other," she said. "This life is no good for me, so it's no good for you *with* me. I know it's hard for you to understand, but I can't become the performer you'd like. It would just be a matter of time until we do again what we did." Her voice became so very, very soft. "We might not be as lucky the next time."

The beauty of our mornings had always been the total absence of conversation—or the need for it—until we made that silent ride to the railway station. Each of us was waiting for the other to have a change of mind. The silent suspense became almost unbearable.

Rita had reservations on the London train, then she was to catch a flight on to Los Angeles. She was only going there to see that the house was put up for sale and to dispose of the furnishings.

I'm sure she'd decided on the train because she had been that certain I would be on it with her. At the last moment, I thought for sure I would be, too. I came that close to folding. Just as I could tell, when she abruptly turned from me and boarded the train, that she had come that close to staying.

I was about to leave the platform when I paused and looked back at the last car. It was an observation car with a glass bubble at the end. And standing in that bubble was Rita.

Obviously, she had followed me down the platform by walking through all those cars and all those people on the train. I could tell by the look on her face she hadn't expected me to turn back. Her eyes were misted, but they didn't have that faraway look. They had the look of a very young girl, frightened and fighting hard not to show it.

I couldn't help thinking, in all the time I'd known her, I couldn't remember her ever being completely alone. It made me wonder how far she would have to go back, if she were to remember the last time she'd set out by herself on such an adventure.

I glanced at that nifty Cartier watch she'd given me. I was signaling that there was still time to get off. She got the message, but she didn't waver. Instead, she managed a smile, and I knew right then I had lost her. It was the first time it hit me that such a thing could actually happen. Then the train started to move. I don't know how long I stood there, watching her get smaller and smaller in that bubble. The train had long gone before I finally turned away.

Across the street from the station was a trattoria. It had a fenced-in patio with umbrella tables that were about half filled. I dropped down at an empty one and ordered a double whiskey. I felt guilty about that, as if as soon as she turned her back, I couldn't wait. After all, I told myself, someone like Rita Hayworth didn't ride out of your life every day.

I dropped the first one at a gulp. After I knocked off the second and was waiting for the waiter to bring me a third, that fragile figure of Rita's, which had grown smaller and smaller in the bubble, began to grow larger in my mind. I got to wondering why she needed me to cope with that brand-new world of hers? After all, this was the girl who'd survived her father, and as if that hadn't sufficiently tested her, she'd taken on Orson Welles.

How she managed to endure that, I'll never know, but she did. Only to wind up with the son of the Aga Khan, which meant assuming the role of princess—a curious transformation for a gypsy. And if all that wasn't enough, along the way she had kept one of the biggest studios afloat with her movies. You remember that it was at that point that I rode to the rescue. But I'd wound up as anxious to use her as all the rest.

So by the time I had polished off that third whiskey, I knew the girl didn't need me, or anyone else. Not when she could survive all that. While she may have looked ever-so-fragile in that diminishing bubble, she was a giant.

I was about to make my way out of the trattoria, because with all that rationalizing, fortified by those doubles, I no longer felt sad, when an old fellow selling flowers approached my table.

"Flowers for your wife?" he asked in his fractured English.

"No wife," I said.

"Your mistress?"

"No way."

"Your girlfriend?"

"I shook my head.

"The girl you've yet to meet?"

Margarita Cansino. That was the name that flashed into my mind. Because that was the girl she was going back to be. That was the girl who was going to paint and forge a brand-new life for herself. That was certainly the girl I'd yet to meet.

The old flower seller must have seen something on my face, because he placed a bouquet on my table. So I gave him a bill and saw that grin of his widen. I ordered another drink and sat staring at the bouquet. Because the girl I'd bought it for—Margarita Cansino— that girl needed all the help she could get.

Margarita Cansino was truly the frightened girl I had watched disappear on the train. A girl as alone and uncertain of her future as a girl could be. No longer the dancing star of the silver screen. No way.

That was when it hit me. Right between the eyes. The only reason I wasn't with her when she needed me most was that I didn't have her brand of moxie. I mean the very thought of putting myself to the test—of actually sitting down to write—scared me to death.

She had said it was my talent for using others that kept me from using my own—those words came back to me then. And I knew that was why I wasn't with her. Nothing to do with my reluctance to leave the red-carpet life for the uncertainties of being on my own. It had to do with the terror of finding out that I really didn't have talent.

Early in my career, even before I met Harry Clork, I'd decided that only a sucker exposed himself by putting words on paper. Then I'd met the greatest of all writers in the business, Vincent Lawrence. He had told me if writing was to be my trade, then pain would be my daily bread.

Those words of his, coupled with my own fears, had all the necessary power to convince me not to pick up a pencil. So there I was, after all those years, faced once again with putting myself to the test, if I wanted to be a part of that brand-new world of Rita's.

I can remember saying to myself, Maybe it would be interesting to go back to the beginning, when I first met her, and start putting my memories down. At least it would be a way to break the ice and maybe get started. I know the notion began to intrigue me enough that I waved the waiter away when he took my glass for a refill. Next thing, I had picked up my bouquet, and that was what I kept thinking about all the way back to the hotel. I'd get some of it down.

Once I found a vase for my flowers, I started pacing and smoking all around them. Even if the writing turned out badly, just doing it might afford a better understanding of both Rita and me. And even if it didn't, I knew that it would make her laugh. That didn't mean it would make anybody else laugh, so maybe that wasn't the commercial way to go about it, but I knew I'd settle for her smile the first time round.

The longer I looked at that bouquet, the more excited I became. While I wasn't doing anything about finding a pencil, I *was* beginning to get all kinds of ideas for the opening.

When I knew I was going to take the risk was when I got to

thinking *beyond* the writing—when I began figuring out our next meeting. I don't mean where I would call her first, or anything like that. I mean where I would just drop by, like when there were no telephones—even if it was raining. And naturally, I'd have the opening pages of my manuscript in one hand, flowers in the other, and the words all ready for her.

"A bouquet for Margarita."